Dear Readers . . .

In 1981, "The People's Friend" introduced a new feature to the magazine. It was called "The Farmer And His Wife" and was a series of country tales told by fictional farmer John Taylor.

To illustrate each story we called upon one of our most popular artists, a gentleman by the name of Douglas Phillips. In his unique, lively and observant style, Doug captured the warm and homely feel of the stories perfectly, and thirty years later the series is still among the most popular features in the magazine.

This souvenir book is a chance for you to enjoy a collection of our favourite stories and illustrations from "The Farmer And His Wife".

Contents

The Early Years

Courting Anne

Life On The Farm

Friends & Family

Out & About

In Anne's Kitchen

The Old Ways

The Man Behind The Stories

READERS of "The People's Friend" were first introduced to "The Farmer And His Wife" in the issue dated May 2, 1981. It was a series of tales of everyday farm life, narrated by fictional farmer John Taylor.

The author of these stories was in fact an architect called Maurice Taylor. He came from a farming background and drew on his knowledge and memories to create the world of the Riggin, set in the East Neuk of Fife.

Fife was a place Maurice knew a great deal about. In 1945 he became Chief Planning Officer there and during his career spearheaded much of the development of modern Fife, creating a more pleasant living environment for the inhabitants.

Maurice wrote as a hobby, and "The Farmer And His Wife" was intended as an occasional series which would appear now and again for a couple of years.

But that, as we know, was not how things turned out! Maurice's writing had a certain magic – he wrote as if he were chatting to his friends round the kitchen table – and readers soon took John and Anne Taylor to their hearts.

John was a living person, hard-working, honest, a bit old-fashioned and rather too fond of his grub. Everything about him, from his struggle with his weight to his relationship with his parents to his disinclination to answer the phone, was credible and relatable.

When John bemoaned the fact that you could no longer buy knitted dishcloths, our postbag overflowed with them – to be passed on to him. The readers sent Christmas cards, recipes and letters to this man with whom they felt such an affinity.

On the face of it, the stories of the Riggin were lighthearted, lightweight articles which brought a bit of fun and humour to the magazine. But the reality was that John Taylor's tales of farming life, married life and days gone by

inspired real affection and emotion in everyone who read them, and "The Farmer And His Wife" fast became the most popular series we have ever run.

Over the years, various editors attempted to replace it with something new. But it reached the point where if it didn't appear, even for one week, letters would pour in demanding to know what had happened to John Taylor.

Over thirty years later, Maurice Taylor's stories are still charming and entertaining readers all over the world and are every bit as popular as they ever were. Maurice himself sadly passed away in 1999 – but John and Anne Taylor live on.

The Man Behind The Drawings

Doug at work.

DOUGLAS PHILLIPS

(1926-2012) was a Dundee lad born and bred, and proud of it.

Although he had studied at Dundee Art College, he was working as an office boy in one of the jute mills when he was called up for the Army, to serve in India and Ceylon.

During this period he still managed to find time to paint and sketch – something which came to the attention of those higher up – and Doug soon found himself engaged in "tactical sketching" for the Army.

When he came back home to Dundee, Doug took a job in the art department of D.C. Thomson & Co. as an illustrator.

"Dad always spoke very fondly of his time in the art department," his daughter, Deborah, says. "Especially all the pranks and high jinks the men got up to!

"He kept up with lots of his colleagues after he left and was friends with many of them until he died."

Although he had enjoyed his time with the company and the variety of work he undertook, including doing illustrations for "The Rover" and "The Victor", just before Deborah was born Doug made the bold decision to leave D.C. Thomson and become a freelance illustrator.

"Some might have seen that as an odd time to leave paid employment," Deborah says with a laugh.

Doug's great talent and his

Towards Todhead From Catterline Cliffs.

Frosty Afternoon, Auchmithie.

incredible work rate, however, ensured he was never short of a commission.

He illustrated over 100 children's books, produced covers for the "Reader's Digest" and held many exhibitions of his own wonderful paintings, many of which are held in private and public collections worldwide.

But here at the "Friend" Doug is remembered with particular affection.

He often dropped into the editorial office, and it was always good to see him.

The designers in particular relished his tales of the old days

More Snow On The Way, Auchmithie.

A Summer Rain Squall.

in the Meadowside art department, and the many colourful characters who worked there.

"Doug was one of our most talented and reliable cover artists," Angela Gilchrist, editor of "The People's Friend", says.

"The only time he ever turned down a commission was in his later years, when he phoned to tell me he was too unwell to tackle the latest cover painting I'd requested. In typical Doug fashion, he fretted that he was letting me down."

In addition to painting over 1,000 covers as J. Campbell Kerr,

Doug also found time to showcase his skills in the magazine's regular "From The Sketchbook Of . . ." feature, with lively pen and ink drawings of some of the many places he loved to visit, including many of the east coast of Scotland and Catterline.

"Dad loved to travel. He enjoyed his holidays and was particularly fond of Italy," Deborah says. "But every trip was spent painting or sketching – nothing else captured his interest in the same way.

"He converted our attic into a studio but it became more of a 'den' – he was often to be found up there with the Velux window open, enjoying a cigar."

Doug passed his talents on to Deborah, who is also an artist.

"I was an only child and Dad and I were very close," she says. "We would go out for a day trip together then come home and paint exactly the same subjects in completely different styles.

"Dad's paintings are still very much in demand and I am still exhibiting his work, which is lovely as it makes me feel I'm keeping his name alive.

"He did lots of work for many of D.C. Thomson's publications but I think it was the 'Friend' that won his heart.

"He saw quite a few editors come and go, and I know he would be absolutely delighted to think that people were still enjoying his work and remembering him so fondly."

Doug and Deborah.

The Early Years

If At First You Don't Succeed . . .

I never give up trying to get Anne to take a step into the past!

CAN you remember the things you did when you were young better than you can remember what happened last week? I certainly can.

We often went to Granny's for Sunday dinner. The highlight was the meat course.

A tall, brown earthenware pot with a lid was put on the table. It stood on a board so as not to mark the cloth or the wood.

It was a hot-pot, with layers of meat and layers of potatoes and vegetables. To me it was out of this world.

I loved Granny and liked to go and stay on their farm when I was a boy. She got me to help – I suppose to keep me out of mischief – cutting up her yard of salt.

She didn't buy it in wee dribbles, but in a block, and kept it in the cellar with the flitches and hams.

She bought flour in half-hundredweight bags. The bags were washed and made into pillow-cases. They did all their own baking in those days.

In the evenings they either knitted or made rag rugs. Times were hard and every penny counted.

Behind one of the doors in the larder were two bags. Into one went any old rags and into the other every piece of string that might be reusable.

When a parcel arrived, the string was carefully removed. It was never cut, no matter how long it took. Every parcel was tied with string then – there was no sticky tape in those days.

The brown paper was then smoothed out and put under the cushions on the long oak settle to be used again at a later date.

When there was enough material for a rug, two of the girls would sit and cut the rags into suitable lengths for pegging. Out came the wooden frame and on it was stretched a hessian bag.

Four people could sit round that frame and, in a few nights, they would have made a beautifully patterned rug.

Anne loved visiting Granny, too, and says I mustn't forget to tell you about how Granny used to buy eggs when they fell below a penny each.

She used to put them in lime water in a big brown earthenware jar for winter.

The flitches and hams which hung on hooks from her kitchen ceiling fascinated me, but Anne won't hear of me hanging them in ours. I keep suggesting it – she keeps saying no.

Come to think of it, I haven't mentioned it for a while. Maybe she's changed her mind by now.

Who knows? And I'm nothing if not a trier – especially where food is concerned! ▪

The Day He Plundered The Orchard . . .

. . . had memorable
and far-reaching effects!

DURING the two-month spell that Anne spent in hospital once, I did for myself. Mary popped in from time to time to make sure the old man was eating properly and hadn't turned her mother's kitchen into a pigsty.

She needn't have worried. I kept the kitchen spotless and, as for eating, I fared even better than when Anne was at home trying to curb my intake!

It was this eating business that set me off on this story . . .

When I was in a greengrocer's in St Andrews, I bought some Victoria plums, ate a few on the way home and stewed the rest.

And what goes with stewed plums? Custard, of course!

Anne always has a tin in the cupboard, so I made myself some lovely, runny custard that perfectly complemented my plums.

When I was a boy, we had an orchard on our farm — plums, cherries and apples in abundance. One summer, when I was about eleven, I ate and ate those apples.

Then I developed a horrible cough.

In those days, you had to be really ill to go to a doctor, especially if you lived out in the country. If the doctor came to the farm, he charged £1 for his travel and five shillings for his diagnosis.

As £1 was a great deal of money, Mother took me to Anstruther in the trap.

The doctor sounded my chest and said, "There's nothing wrong with the boy. Have you been eating apples?"

"Yes, sir."

"Don't eat any more for a week."

Mother put her five shillings in the plate and, boy, did I catch it as we trotted home!

Five shillings to be told I had eaten too many apples! It was more than she could stomach!

Apples might have been my downfall then, but plums were my saving grace when I got a phone call to say our son and his wife were visiting Anne on the Sunday. Anne issued instructions from her hospital bed in the afternoon.

"Give them a meal — they're coming all the way from Edinburgh."

Well, I decided we'd have cold meat and salad, so it wouldn't matter when they rolled in.

After leaving Anne, I went back to the greengrocer's in St Andrews for some more plums.

I arrived just as one of the assistants was unloading a lorry, and was coming through the shop with a boxful.

"How much for the lot?" I said.

A price was quickly agreed, and I went back to the Riggin with twelve pounds of beautiful Victoria plums. The result — I stewed some and put three lots in the freezer.

Our son and daughter-in-law can have some, with my special custard. Anne can make plum jam for the church sales and I can defrost some and enjoy stewed plums and custard whenever I want! ■

A Man Of Means!

My first big business deal was one to be proud of!

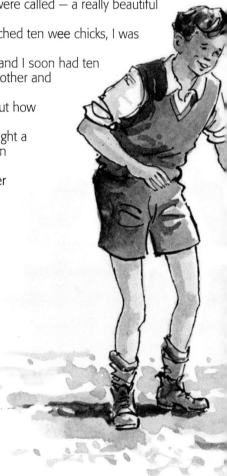

WHEN I was twelve years old, I kept a bantam hen and cock. Old English Game, they were called — a really beautiful pair of birds.

When the hen laid eggs and hatched ten wee chicks, I was delighted — my first flock!

They grew up over the summer and I soon had ten young birds as beautiful as their mother and father.

I thought I should sell some — but how would I do that?

In September, the postman brought a catalogue from Gamages in London addressed to Mother.

How they got her name we never discovered. If she knew she certainly wasn't telling us.

We pored over that catalogue, and Dad noticed that they had a zoo. Not only did they sell animals, they bought them as well.

Dad suggested I write and ask them if they would buy two bantam cocks.

I had never written a letter before, and it was quite a test. I did it three times before I was happy and Dad said it was suitable to send.

London seemed so far away in those days. A trip to Dundee was foreign travel when I was a boy!

But I posted my letter all the way to London, and how thrilled I was when I received their reply — a real letter addressed to me!

Yes, they would be pleased to buy my bantams at five shillings each — a lot of money in 1928. But how was I going to get them to London?

Dad came to my rescue once again and made a travelling box that was a work of art. Gamages must have liked it, too — they never sent it back!

In those days, you sent animals by train. Dad agreed to drive me and the bantams to Kingsbarns station after he had finished doing the milking.

Today we'd just jump in a car, but in those days it meant harnessing Prince the pony and driving there in the trap.

It all took time and it was quite a journey.

That's one of the things I remember most fondly about the days of my childhood.

Yes, we were always busy — yes, there was always another job to be attended to.

But there was none of the rushing around you see so much of these days. We attended to each job in order but there always seemed to be time for everything.

Anyway, we set off, and Dad enjoyed looking at all the other farmers' crops and stock as we passed.

When we reached the station, I waited for the train and rushed over to the guard to tell him my story.

"I'll look after them, laddie," he assured me kindly. "They'll be in London about seven o'clock tomorrow evening."

They must have arrived all right because in due course I received my postal order for ten shillings.

Would anyone today have gone to so much trouble to earn ten shillings — fifty pence?

But to me, ten shillings was a lot of money — and it was all my own!

The Right Connections

Do you remember the days when the phone was a lot more fun?

CAN'T remember exactly when it was, but it must have been round about 1928 when we got a phone installed at the farm. Dad couldn't have cared less about being connected to the outside world – he was a real homebody – but Mother was different.

She had heard on good authority that Mrs McAndrew was having a phone put in and Mother wasn't about to be done down! We would have to have one, too!

The only way to do that in those days was to join a party line. It seems incredible in this day and age, but it's true.

In the end, about eight of us joined in the party line. That meant that if the phone rang three times, it was for us – but three other families would be listening in!

The other snag was actually trying to make a call. The phone was silent and you picked it up to ring a friend, but Mrs McAndrew was already on the line, chattering nineteen to the dozen.

How many phone calls were overheard, I never found out – but I have little doubt most of the information was soon passed around the district "in strictest confidence".

I wish I had kept a copy of my old folks' phone bills. If it ever came to over two pounds it would caused a real rumpus.

Dad would be heard to say, "Let's have it taken out!"

Not on your life! As far as Mother was concerned, if Mrs McAndrew had a phone then we had to have one as well!

In any case, I think she got more than her money's worth, either contributing to or listening to all the local gossip. I think she almost preferred it when someone else was on the line!

I'd often watch Ma. She'd put her hand over the receiver so no-one knew she was listening as she enjoyed all the scandal!

Of course, everyone has a phone these days. Don't I know it. But ours is most certainly not a party line.

It's the exclusive property – or so it seems – of Mrs Anne Taylor. She's the one who gets most use out of it, anyway. I don't even like

answering the thing.

And like my father, I am always heard to complain when the bill comes in. I sometimes think Anne would be disappointed if I didn't say something.

Her reply is always the same.

"I don't drink, I don't smoke, I don't gamble, and when did you last take me out for a meal? If I can't even have a chat on the phone, things have come to a pretty pass!"

Then she tilts her head to the side like a belligerent wee robin and dares me to contradict her.

And she's right. I can't.

All right, all right, where did I put my cheque book? I'll pay the darned bill . . . ▪

A Rainbow-coloured Memory

Clearing out a drawer took me on an unexpected trip back to childhood.

J**OHN**! John!" The voice from the bathroom became louder and more insistent.

Why do wives call at the most awkward moments — and expect an answer right away? I had one leg in my trousers and the other suspended in mid-air!

As soon as I could walk I scuttled along to the bathroom.

"What took you so long?"

I chose not to answer. Anything I might have said would certainly have been taken the wrong way.

"What is it, dear?"

"Go and find me another petticoat. The strap's broken on this one."

I smiled to myself and said nothing.

I'm getting older and wiser — and I'm learning when to hold my tongue.

But between you and me, I don't think Anne possesses a slip with both straps still attached.

The makers of safety pins will always have a market while she's around.

I looked in the wardrobe, but it was all dresses and things. So I went over to the chest of drawers and opened the bottom one first.

Well, it was crammed full of what looked like junk to me — it was obviously Anne's "treasure" drawer.

I was holding something when she came sailing into the room.

"You won't find any petticoats in there!" she told me.

Before I could show her what I had found, she had grabbed another slip from a different drawer and sailed out again, slamming the door behind her.

I looked again at my find.

To anyone else, it was just a coloured woollen ball. About six inches across, all the colours of the rainbow, with a pleated cord about a foot long.

I had been about seven at the time and there was a big drive on to raise money for the church.

I knew that, with two round pieces of cardboard and lots of wool and patience, you could make a pompom ball.

It took me a long time, but eventually it was finished. Mother suggested I take it to a farmer's wife near Crail, and she gave me one shilling and threepence for my efforts.

I think Mother must have arranged the sale, because the lady had no children to play with the pompom.

Twenty years later, Anne and I had our first child, who received one pompom ball as a present.

It was all the colours of the rainbow — and still in the brown paper bag which I had proudly carried over the fields! ■

A Hair-raising Experience!

I'll never forget the barber who made my hair stand on end before he cut it!

I WAS wondering what to write about this week. Anne was sitting in her Orkney chair when I mentioned my predicament.

"Why not tell them about your haircut in Leigh?" she asked, having heard the story many times.

So here goes . . .

We drove down in a Swift car with a wooden frame. As we were entering Leigh, my mother said, "Boy, you can't go to see my relatives looking like that."

She had just noticed my hair. I suppose my "Just William" hairstyle was OK for a farm in Fife, but not for the posh cousins in Leigh.

Posh, my foot. I've often wondered why so many country folk think that someone who wears a collar and tie and works in an office is a superior.

My mother's relations were, I learned later, plumbers.

They might have been able to stick two pipes together, but could they milk a cow or help a calf come into the world? Not likely!

Anyway, Mother instructed Father to look for a barber's shop as we approached Leigh.

Dad saw one of the red and white barber's poles protruding from a wall. He stopped the car, gave me threepence and told me to go into the shop.

I went down three steps, opened a door, and a cloud of black pipe smoke engulfed me.

Two gas lights lit the room. There were two men cutting hair, or rather shearing heads. Men sat on benches round the room; men with dirty black faces and wearing clogs.

A man moved across from the bench to the cutting chair.

The barber ran his hand-operated cutting machine right across his head, as though he were shearing a sheep. He didn't leave him with a hair on his head!

I was panic-stricken. I would have liked to have run away but I was frightened of what my parents might say.

My turn came. I went and sat in the chair — trembling.

"Please, sir, I don't want all my hair cut off!"

The whole room — barbers and men — laughed heartily.

"Laddie, when tha's old enough to go down t'pit then I'll take thy hair off."

He gave me a trim and I gave him the threepence. He handed me a penny back.

It's an experience I've never forgotten. But I still wonder if Mother's relations noticed my twopenny haircut!

I went for another haircut recently, and it cost a lot more than tuppence!

"Did you tip him?" Anne asked.

You wouldn't print my reply! ■

John keeps a meadow to encourage the bees.

Courting Anne

The Day I Won A Prize

I had hoped for at least second place – but I went home with the Best In Show!

HIGHLY Commended. I couldn't believe my eyes.

The way the stonemason had been so enthusiastic about my bantam hen taking a prize at Cupar show, I was convinced it could have had a winning ticket.

After all, he knew his hens – he was a breeder and a judge!

But, no, not even a second place. I was so disappointed I nearly burst into tears.

I wanted to go home there and then, but entries weren't to be removed from the show until 4.30 p.m.

The birds were in cages, stacked two high, on long trestle tables. I was gloomily studying my hen, and the ones who had beaten her, when I happened to look up.

Through the cages at the other side, a pretty young lady smiled at me.

I suppose I should have said hello, but I have to admit that I was more than a little frightened of young ladies in those days, so the moment was lost.

On the dot of 4.30 p.m., my hen was taken out of her cage, put into a crate and loaded on to my bicycle. I left the showground in a despondent mood.

I'd just passed the Pitscottie crossroads and was heading for Peat Inn. As I rounded the bend, I saw a lassie pushing her cycle up the steep hill.

I drew alongside and dismounted.

"Hello, John – I see you won a prize at the show."

It was the same lassie I had seen by the cages. And she was one up on me – she knew my name!

I'd never known what to say to a girl before. Being an only child can be a distinct disadvantage.

Mother wasn't a great one for socialising and I had really only known the company of family and the farm workers.

But, that evening, as we pushed our bikes up the hill to Peat Inn, I

found I could talk to this smiling, unmade-up young lady whom I had never met before.

I learned she had two brothers and two sisters and, as she was the eldest girl, she knew how to deal with boys.

Chatting posed her no problem. She didn't even seem to notice my shyness and that I was more than a little tongue-tied.

"Did you have anything in the show?"

I'll never know what prompted me to ask that, but thank goodness I did.

She had a third for blackberry and apple jam and a first for raspberry sponge, but I still didn't know her name.

We could have ridden our bikes part of the way, but we didn't. It seemed more natural to walk and chat.

Then, when we reached Peat Inn, I should have gone left to Crail, but I didn't.

It was this decision to take the right-hand path that changed the whole course of my life . . . for the better and for happiness. ■

31

Identity Crisis

From the moment I met her, I knew she was the girl for me. The only trouble was, I didn't know her name!

YOU may remember that recently I told you about how Anne and I met on the way home from the Cupar show.

That, of course, was many moons ago, and we have celebrated our golden wedding.

Does the Almighty look down on young couples and guide them in the way they should go? I think He guided Anne and me that evening, as He has done ever since.

I was seventeen years old and in all my life I'd never met anyone that I could talk to or confide in before. Walking home with Anne that evening, she made it seem so easy.

Eventually we came to their farm gate. The farmhouse lay just over half a mile up the lane.

Looking back, I wonder why I didn't say goodnight and ride on, but to be honest I didn't want to leave the lassie until I had to.

I opened the gate and we pushed our cycles through — mine with a "highly commended" bantam hen on the back, hers with a large basket with a lid. We propped our cycles against the wall and she opened her basket.

We sat on the bank and shared some of her prize-winning sandwich cake.

It must have been about half an hour later when her younger brother turned up. He, too, propped his cycle against the wall and settled down beside us to enjoy some cake.

Brother and sister went their way and I went mine. I was determined to meet her again, but there was one problem — I didn't know her name.

She already knew mine, so I didn't like to come straight out and ask her.

As I put the sneck on the gate I noted the farm name. My problem was twofold — how to find out her name and how to contrive to meet her again.

As I lay in bed that night I decided to ask Mr Calder, Dad's pal. He had invited me down to his farm to look over his stock.

I cycled down one evening and we made a tour of his farm.

"Mr Calder, if I tell you something, you won't say anything to my mum and dad, will you?"

He smiled.

"No, John, I won't."

I told him all about riding home from the Cupar show and meeting this young lady. When I mentioned the name of the farm, he knew the family straight away.

"Laddie, that's Jim McDonald's place. A good farmer, doesn't owe a penny. And his wife, Alice, is a grand woman. Sorry, though, John, I don't know the girl's name."

Four days later, at lunchtime, the phone rang. Mother answered.

"It's for you, John."

A phone call for me was unheard of in those days. Mother was all ears!

"I'll be down to see it soon. Thanks a lot," was all I said.

"Who was that?" she asked, the minute I put the phone down.

"Mr Calder," I replied.

"What did he want?" she persisted.

"Nothing much. He just rang to tell me that a heifer we were looking at the other night had had a calf."

"Oh!" she said, obviously disappointed that the call had not been more interesting.

But of course it was! Jim Calder had used the news of the calf as an excuse to phone and say, "John, her name's Anne." ■

"I Can Explain!"

Looking back to my courtship with Anne, it's clear that the road to true love wasn't always a smooth one!

D AD knew that I was seeing Anne, but we hadn't told Mother. She was determined I wasn't going to marry a country lassie if she could help it.

Inevitably, though, she eventually found out about Anne and me – how, I still don't know – and, sad to say, she set out to break up our friendship.

One day, as we were driving through St Andrews on our way to Dundee, she told me to turn into Hope Street as she wanted to call on a friend.

As I didn't expect her to be long, I waited in the car, and shortly after she came back with a young girl about my own age.

"Jump in the front beside John," Mother told her, before I could say anything.

I wasn't best pleased, but there was nothing I could do without being rude to the lassie, so we carried on.

There was no bridge to Dundee in those days, so we had to wait for a ferry at Newport.

As I was later to discover, and as Mother had no doubt hoped, someone saw me there, with a young lady beside me.

They put two and two together, came up with five, and lost no time in reporting back to Anne.

We were late doing the milking on the Sunday and consequently I was late getting to church that evening.

I slid into the pew beside Anne and whispered my apology.

But all she said was, "Have you been having tea in St Andrews?"

After the service I tried to explain, but she would have none of it. In despair, I went to see Dad's pals, Jim and Mabel, and poured out the whole story.

Jim was furious. He knew Anne and liked her, and I guess he didn't like the thought of her feelings being hurt in that way – and over nothing at all.

He promised to have a word with Mother and sort things out.

I was a bit unsure about this, if I'm being honest. Mother was a formidable woman and didn't like anyone telling her what to do –

especially people who weren't even family. And she wasn't shy about expressing herself, either.

I thought a lot of Jim and hated to think that Mother might be rude to him.

At lunchtime the next day the phone rang, and it was Anne.

"Can you be at the bottom gate at seven?"

I was over the moon.

Much later, I learned that Jim had talked to Mother and had really laid it on the line.

He warned her not to ruin my life by spoiling my chances with Anne, or she risked losing me altogether.

And as if this good deed wasn't enough, he had gone the extra mile and had also paid a visit to Anne and explained things to her.

"Let's go and visit Jim and thank him," I said.

So we did. And he and his lovely wife Mabel were so pleased to see us!

I shook Jim's hand and thanked him, but Anne stood on her tiptoes, put her arms around him and gave that big hulk of a farmer a great big kiss.

And I couldn't help noticing a tear in Jim's eye as he gave Anne a squeeze. ■

Emergency Operation

I wasn't about to let even an injury interrupt my date with Anne!

A S I came across the yard to the back door the other day, I sneezed. I had been scattering a bale of hay to some young stock and some of the hay dust must have got up my nose.

I sneezed again. Suddenly, blood came streaming down my nose.

Anne got a towel, wet it and held my nose tightly for a couple of minutes. It stopped.

I admit I treated it with respect for the rest of the evening.

It reminded me of the last time that my nose had caused me bother.

It was mid-July 1933 – we were well on with the hay when for no reason other than I was hot – very hot – my nose started to bleed.

Could we stop it? Not on your life!

Dad and I went back to the house. Keys, cold water, pinching it tightly – nothing worked.

Mother was getting worried, I could tell, although she was trying hard to convince me it would stop any minute. I was scared and I think that made it worse.

Dad got out the car and we shot off at top speed to the hospital at St Andrews in our working clothes – me with a towel at my nose.

Thank goodness there was a doctor going round the wards who came to my rescue. He stopped it.

The cauterising experience was not one I'd like to go through again, although I understand the procedure is a lot less unpleasant these days.

My nose was packed with a sort of bandage and the doctor instructed me to take it out slowly on the following Monday.

Sunday night was Anne's night – back seat at Kingsbarns Church. If the doctor thought I was going to appear on Sunday night to Anne with a nose full of bandage looking like one of the walking wounded, he was mistaken!

As Dad was outside in the car waiting for me, he didn't know when it had to be removed, and I didn't enlighten him.

I stuck it out till teatime on Sunday and then disappeared to the bathroom.

If you didn't know it, there are thousands of little hairs in your nose. I reckon every single one must have stuck to my gauze.

It was agony, but I didn't dare make a sound, or Mother would have come to see what was happening.

I met Anne before going to church and we cycled to her farm afterwards.

I told her about my nose. She saw the funny side and laughed.

Give her her due, though, she gave me a kiss from a difficult angle that didn't catch my nose. Careful sort, my Anne. ■

Feeling Sheepish

A good turn made all the difference to Anne and me.

MOTHER had just served up lunch when the phone rang. That wasn't unusual. Anyone wanting to speak to Dad knew that there was no point ringing any earlier. He'd be out in the steading or on the land.

Mother said disapprovingly, "It's Jim Calder for you." She didn't like Jim, especially since he'd had words with her about her attitude

towards Anne.

Dad picked up the phone, then afterwards sat down and finished his meal. None of us were any the wiser as to why Jim had rung.

That afternoon, as we were out checking on some young stock, Dad enlightened me.

Jim was going to the ram sales in Lanark and had asked if I might drive him there. Dad had said I would.

Jim was perfectly capable of driving himself to Lanark, so I suspected an ulterior motive. He'd always been very kind to me. I reckoned he would use the day to teach me a bit about rams.

On the journey to Lanark, Jim enquired whether I had asked Anne to marry me.

"Not yet, but I hope to, some day."

"How much money do you have, John?"

I told him about a hundred pounds.

"If you get the chance of a farm, come and see me before you take it. Your dad should set you up, but your mother will stop him if she can."

I was only too aware of this fact.

When we arrived at the sale, I noted the number of the ram Jim wanted, and learned a bit about bidding as the auction took place.

We left the ring and went to have lunch at the Royal Hotel where Jim introduced me to a farmer from Rannoch. They discussed farming and bargained over a wee whisky. By the time lunch was over, Jim had bought eighty gimmer lambs.

Jim's car was a big American brute — I can't remember the name, but we put the ram in the back — no bother at all.

On the way home, Jim told me that the farmer who usually took his winter field had died. Jim asked if I would like to take it.

"I'd love to, but I haven't any sheep."

"Well, I bought you eighty gimmer lambs today, from Rannoch."

My heart skipped a beat. I hadn't enough money to pay for eighty lambs! Jim saw the look on my face and went on.

"You'll be short of cash at first, John, so you may as well make a start now. I'll pay for these lambs in the meantime and you can pay me back next year when you sell them."

Jim Calder's kind gesture was to make a world of difference to Anne and myself. ■

Pretty patchwork fields mark the passing of the farm's year.

Life On The Farm

A Fly In The Ointment

It was an expensive business when I set out to rid the Riggin of pests!

THOSE faceless men in Brussels are putting quotas on sheep. That means that they can tell me – who was rearing sheep before some of them were born – how many sheep I can keep on my farm!

Anne was out and I was sitting at our kitchen table, trying to read "Farmer's Weekly" and learn what I could about the whole business.

I said "trying" – there was one disturbing fly in the ointment, as they say – a big bluebottle buzzing round the kitchen.

If only it would land on the table I would dispatch it to where some of these Brussels men should go!

Until it landed, I daren't take a swipe at it. I've learned that such actions can have serious consequences!

One of Anne's most treasured possessions is her collection of Royal Doulton figures, plus the bigger balloon lady.

One fateful day I swiped off one which had been a present to Anne from our daughter, Mary. It was in atoms on the hearth, and Anne was in tears.

I hot-footed it to our local china shop and, luckily, they had the same lady in stock.

I'm sorry to say that was not the only time I've broken one of Anne's treasures. It must have been about two years after we were married, because Anne was expecting our first child.

I well remember it was a Saturday morning, just after eight. I had just finished the milking and had come in for my breakfast.

Anne gave me real breakfasts in those days – porridge, followed by bacon, eggs, black pudding, tomatoes and toast.

Anne was on her knees on the floor.

"There's a mouse behind this cupboard." Anne isn't scared of mice; she just doesn't like them in the kitchen.

As soon as I moved the cupboard, a mouse scuttled out and ran across the floor. Without thinking, I picked up the bread knife and made a swipe at it.

There was a loud crack, and I was left with the wooden handle in my hands.

"Oh, John, that was a wedding present."

A young farmer had made Anne a dark teak breadboard with a groove for the breadknife, and he had fashioned the handle and fitted in a blade. Now it was in two bits.

I never did get my breakfast that morning. I jumped in the buggy and raced to Cupar.

My first stop was Mr Honeyman, the saddler. I put the knife on the counter and told him my sad story. There was a long silence.

"Laddie, I made your catapults and mended your braces, but I cannae put wood and steel together."

Another silence.

"Go to Bob and tell him I sent you. Say I said he was the only man in town who could do it."

Bob the plumber was hard at work when I went in. I showed him the knife and told him what Mr Honeyman had said.

"He said that, did he?" Long pause. "Come back at twelve."

I've never known two hours go so slowly. Eventually, though, I returned, and there he was, holding the knife, which was all in one piece.

"Well, John, I've done it. You can go and tell Honeyman he was right enough."

I raced back to the Riggin. Anne was worried – she thought I'd run away for good! When I showed her the knife, she gave me a big hug and a kiss.

The breakages we've sustained over the years due to my over-enthusiastic fly-swatting made me wonder what happened to the sticky fly-paper Gran always had in her kitchen in the summer. I suppose it's a thing of the past.

By the way, that bluebottle is also a thing of the past – thanks to a swipe from my "Farmer's Weekly"! ▧

45

Manners Maketh Man!

I well remember the time I had to brace myself for an etiquette lesson!

WHEN I married Anne, I quickly realised there were certain things one didn't do – well, not in company. Especially not, I might add, in front of Anne's bridge friends!

The first is eating soup. You tip the plate away from you, not towards you. Don't ask me why.

There are also certain ways to hold a knife, apparently. Anne says you can always tell whether someone has been well brought up by the way they hold their knife.

Clothing is another subject Anne is strict about. She wouldn't, for example, go to church without wearing a hat, but she can't explain why – she just says her mother never did!

So what started me off on this dos and don'ts story? It was a simple but essential thing for a man of my size – a pair of braces!

Austin, one of our grandsons, had just left school and wanted to start his own flock of sheep on his dad's farm. He wanted me to sell him four of my lambs before auction.

We had done the inspection and were standing in the yard when a car came through the top gate. To my horror, it was one of Anne's bridge friends! And me standing there with no coat on and my braces over my shirt! Definitely not a thing to do in company . . .

Much to Austin's amusement, I slipped my braces off and threw them over the wall before I went inside to be polite.

Next morning I searched high and low but couldn't find my braces anywhere. I had to tie a piece of baling twine round my middle, and Anne was not amused!

When Anne went to see to her hens, I rang Austin. How he laughed!

"They're in the manger, Grandad," he told me. And so they were.

Recently I bought the largest pair of braces they had in a shop in St Andrews. Unfortunately, they were clip-on braces, and you know how I feel about them! But try to buy a pair of trousers with buttons for braces – it's next to impossible!

Anne had goaded me into entering a gents' outfitters which, according to their advert in the local paper, had trousers in my size. I chose two pairs.

The young man was wrapping them up when I noticed they hadn't buttons for braces. I told the salesman they were no good to me like that!

"No bother, sir. We can put them on."

"At no extra cost?"

He quoted a figure, and added postage. I told him to wrap them up and I'd sew the buttons on myself!

A couple of nights later I undid my brand-new braces and let my trousers fall to the floor. Then I struggled to get my big feet out of them.

I heard a snap. I'd put eighteen stones down on one of the clips and broken it.

Next day, I tried to fix it with pliers. No use. At this stage, most men would have put the braces in the dustbin. Not John Taylor. I never throw anything away that might be useful.

In a drawer in my wardrobe I keep odds and ends that might come in useful some day – including old braces. I picked a clip that looked OK and sewed it on.

Unfortunately, that clip didn't work very well. I only had to bend over and it went "ping"!

Anne and I took a trip into St Andrews and, as I bent over to lock the car, my braces went "ping". Even worse, the back clip did the same!

Anne didn't notice anything until we stopped to talk to one of her friends.

"John, take your hands out of your pockets!" she hissed.

"If I do, my breeks will be round my ankles!"

Luckily Anne has a sense of humour.

"That'll be a treat for the people of St Andrews!"

As soon as we got home I sewed the buttons on those trousers and dug out my last pair of buttoning braces. They're going to be used every day from now on. ■

It's A Fine Life!

Anne and I enjoy taking a
few moments to count our blessings.

THE phone rang at about half-past eight on a Saturday night. I was looking at the evening paper, so Anne went to answer, as usual. It was our granddaughter, who'd been visiting us that day.

"Hello, dear. You're safely home, then?"

Anne relayed the conversation to me after the call was over.

"Gran, thank you for a wonderful afternoon. I did enjoy myself. Here's Mum."

Anne chatted to our daughter for a few minutes. (Well, it was twenty, really, but I can't say anything. Anne says she doesn't smoke or drink, so if she can't have a blether on the phone then it's a sad state of affairs.)

Two days afterwards, we got a note from our son saying how much our granddaughter had enjoyed her afternoon with Gran.

Grandads don't really exist. It's Gran who is the important one.

The little girl only came for a few hours while her mum attended to some business in St Andrews, but she had a day with Gran that she would always remember.

I suppose, if you live in a town, there are lots of interesting things going on on a farm.

She helped Gran collect the eggs, then they looked at the lambs and she helped – or so she thought, bless her – to feed the calves.

Anne and I were chatting about it later, and we came to the happy conclusion that we were very fortunate.

We are fortunate to be tillers of the soil and carers of the animals. It is a very satisfying life. You do have to come to terms with the fact that the animals are headed for the butcher's shop, but I like to think that although their lives are short, they are happy ones.

We are fortunate to have five grandchildren who all think the world of my Anne.

One of our grandsons, having been denied something or other by his own parents, huffily asserted that he would phone Gran and ask her for it instead! So he did – and Anne, not knowing his parents had said no, said yes!

Our son laughingly complains that his children get far better treatment than he ever did!

Well, we haven't much money at the moment, with farming going through a bad patch, but we had even less when our bairns were growing up, so naturally they didn't get so much.

"What will they do when we die?"

That remark was Anne's as she sat in her Orkney chair, gazing into the fire. She didn't seem too worried by the prospect.

I said nothing. There are times when even I know to keep my mouth shut. I could have repeated what her old dad used to say in answer to the same question: "Children, you'll just have to carry on yourselves."

How true – and we did.

Our grandchildren will make their own way splendidly, I'm sure – but we'll continue to spoil them while we can! ■

Keeping The Home Fires Burning

**It's sad to see old trees blown down –
but it warms your heart to think of
the logs they will provide!**

ON the eastern boundary of our farm, there's a burn that, over hundreds of years, has worn a channel down to the rocks, leaving sloping sides, now covered with trees.

I love to walk along its top bank with Jip, our sheepdog, taking time to appreciate the ferns, flowers and wildlife.

The other day there was a pair of dippers sitting on two rocks. When they spotted us, they dived down into the water and came to the surface further upstream. They're so entertaining to watch as they bob up and down while perching on a rock.

Dippers always remind me of waiters dressed in long-tailed evening jackets and white shirts. All they lack is a black bow-tie.

A sadder sight was the three old trees blown down in the winter gales. I made a mental note to recover them for firewood – nothing beats a log fire for cheer, especially at this time of the year.

If we have a party, and that doesn't happen often now, Anne insists we have a log fire burning in the lounge.

In my young days, when money was scarce, we burned little coal, but a lot of wood. If there was a fallen tree, we'd hitch two horses and fasten a chain to the tree and haul it home.

Over the next few nights, Dad and I would saw the tree into suitable lengths, using a two-handed cross-cut saw.

Then, with a long-handled axe, we'd split the wood into smaller-sized logs for the fire. Hard labour? It certainly was! But in those days we looked on it as just another winter task.

Did I ever tell you about the sale of effects of Mrs Purves of Earlshall? Anne and I went along, not intending to buy anything.

However, as we walked into the sale, Anne took a paddle from the girl on the door. Against its number the girl listed Anne's name and address.

When a big copper cauldron came under the hammer, Anne waited until the last moment to make her bid and it was knocked down to her.

I asked Anne why she'd bought it. She gave me one of her looks and said it would make a lovely log basket for the lounge.

She was right, of course. Now full of logs, it sits beside our fire and looks the part.

Coming back to those fallen trees by the burn, I thought of how things had changed since my dad's day. Now there is no need for chains and horses to haul the trees home.

I went back to the farm for the forklift and the chainsaw. I cut the trees into three lengths and brought them back on the forklift.

In the yard I cut them into small lengths, and the result was enough logs to keep our lounge fire roaring for about ten years!

I wonder if I can persuade Anne to have a few dinner parties to use up our fallen trees? ■

Counting Sheep

No, I wasn't suffering from insomnia – it was lambing time!

THERE was a bitter wind blowing from the east – probably all the way from Siberia. It was half-past six of a morning in April and Anne said she would come with me on the first round of the lambing ewes.

First we had mugs of tea and warm, well-buttered toast – brown bread which Anne makes herself.

Anne has, for my sake, so she says, cut out the sugar in my tea. It's surprising how quickly you get used to something – I wouldn't thank you for tea with sugar in it now.

As we left the warmth of the kitchen, we locked the back door and put the key in a gutter by the pig sty. With two crooks, we set out, taking Jip with us.

Two black-faced ewes had, since we were round just before midnight, given birth to twins. We were pleased, as black-faced ewes only usually have one lamb.

They were all on their feet and had found their mothers' milk.

We have a number of cross-bred Cheviot-Border Leicester sheep. One of the ewes was lying down at full stretch under a small hummock.

She stretched, got up and lay down again. Anne wanted to help her, but I said we should just wait and see. She was a good, upstanding ewe and there was no reason why she shouldn't have a normal delivery.

Then she stood up, and out popped a lamb into the cold world. There wasn't a prouder mother. She licked her small offspring and got it to breathe. It wobbled on its long legs, looking very helpless.

Anne was worried – should she get it to suck?

I said to wait. A big sheep like that should have two lambs. About fifteen minutes later, the ewe lay down again, and out dropped a second lamb.

As soon as we saw they had both found the teat, we went round the rest of the flock.

One sheep, on the far side of the meadow, had given birth to three lambs. A sheep has a job feeding three, but now we knew, if a single lamb died at birth, there was a lamb the sheep could mother on to.

Well, it hadn't been a bad lambing time. At least it had been dry, but oh, so cold.

A lamb can stand the cold, but to be dropped into a rainfall on the rain-soaked earth is sometimes too much for them.

As it happened, a black-faced sheep did lose her lamb, so we mothered that third lamb on to her.

We skinned the dead lamb and put the skin on the back of the substitute lamb. Give the mother her due, she took to it straight away.

It's a hard time of the year, but one I always enjoy. To me there's no finer sight than a little lamb's tail going nineteen to the dozen as it takes its very first drink of milk! ■

A Built-up Area

The skills I learned from my father stood me in good stead one day.

J OHN, you're late. I was getting worried!"

I suppose Anne and I are old-fashioned. If she's late getting back from a meeting or shopping, I worry. She does the same about me. Silly, I suppose, but that's how we are.

I was late that night, and tired and cold. It was half-past six and I'm usually in for tea about five.

"I wanted to finish that wall. I couldn't face going back to it tomorrow."

I knew what had happened to damage the wall. A loose dog had been roaming around our top land and the sheep had taken fright and bolted.

They'd jumped the wall, dislodging one of the top stones. As sheep followed sheep, they made a gap in the wall.

If there's one thing that irritates me, it's the state of far too many walls. Gaps are stopped by putting posts and wire netting across or, worse still, sheets of corrugated iron.

Labour, I know, is not cheap today. What's more, finding a man who has the skill to repair a drystane dyke isn't easy. It's what I would call a dying art form.

I'm fortunate. My father was an expert dyker and I used to go and labour for him. I have never matched his skill, but I learned how it was done.

If built properly, each stone is part of a regular course, and slopes downwards and outwards from the centre of the dyke.

The centre is filled with wee stones, then the whole lot topped with stones carefully wedged together.

That night I was cold, tired, and glad to be back in Anne's warm kitchen. She knows when a man needs a good feed. She spread before me a meal that was no good for my figure, but had an amazing effect on my morale.

Tucking into bacon, two eggs and some rounds of black pudding, I soon forgot my aches and pains.

I had used some muscles not usually asked to work, and I was going to suffer for it the next day, but I was pleased with my efforts.

Some of us still have pride in our land and our walls. That's something else I inherited from my father.

He taught me that a stitch in time saves nine. Especially where walls and fences are concerned.

An afternoon's labour today can save you a couple of days' work further down the line. And usually a lot of expense as well.

I went to bed a tired man, but I slept well, knowing that the gap which had annoyed me for weeks was tidily repaired.

But, please, if you are out enjoying the countryside with your dog this weekend, remember to keep it on the lead, or at least keep it under control.

Old, overweight farmers have better things to do with their time than to stand out in the cold and wet repairing drystane dykes! ■

A Bit Of A Wag

Jip may never win any sheepdog trials, but I wouldn't have swapped her for the world.

WHEN Jip, our faithful sheepdog, was going with me round the sheep one day, she kept stopping and rubbing her ears on the ground.

I know she makes out she's going deaf from time to time when she pretends not to hear me calling, but this was different. Something was bothering her.

I told Anne when we got back to the house and she immediately made an appointment at the vet's in Cupar.

Anne and I are careful sorts, but if Jip was suffering, no expense would be spared trying to help her.

Jip was no spring chicken at that time – she would be twelve, or even thirteen, we reckoned. But the point is, she was far more than just a sheepdog.

Truth be told, she wasn't really a sheepdog in the true sense of the phrase.

What I mean is, although she accompanied me round the farm and treated all the animals with respect, she had never been taught to herd sheep or obey a shepherd's commands.

She was a faithful friend and companion for both Anne and me, and could convey so much with her eyes and tail. If you're a dog person you'll know what I mean.

Any time I was going somewhere in the tractor she begged to come, so I would lift her up into the cab where she would sit, keeping a watchful eye on what was going on.

She seemed to enjoy being up high and having a good view of everything.

Well, Anne took Jip to the vet and came away with a plastic bottle of ointment to scoot in Jip's ears. She had an ear infection – nothing serious but quite uncomfortable.

I'm pleased to say the ointment did the trick and was well worth the expense.

One evening, Anne and I sat watching "One Man And His Dog" on television. It's a programme we both particularly enjoy.

When it was over we switched off and Anne said jokingly, "John, why

don't you and Jip enter?"

The very thought made me laugh. It would certainly have made for very entertaining viewing!

I could just hear the presenter saying, "Sorry, John, Jip didn't actually find the sheep!"

Even if she had found them, I couldn't see her bringing them in a straight line to the gate.

No, Jip and I wouldn't have dreamed of entering. We never even attempted any local trials.

The next time Jip and I jumped into the tractor and headed for the top fields, I told her about Anne's suggestion for "One Man And His Dog".

I don't think she understood – but, bless her, she still wagged her tail! ■

Kidding Around!

When I was asked if I wanted a goat for my birthday, I said no – and no buts about it!

WHY is it that people always ring you at meal times? If it happens in our house I just leave the phone ringing – if it's important they'll call back.

Anne says she can't enjoy her food with the phone going in the background. She needs to know who is calling and for what. I think she's scared she misses something!

We had just finished our tea the other night when Anne had to answer the phone.

I had spread my paper on the table to catch up on the news and to look at the agriculture page.

It soon became clear that the caller was Alice, a farmer's wife she was friendly with. They met years ago at the WRI and they hit it off straight away.

We have often been round to their farm for dinner and Alice's roast beef is out of this world.

"John, Alice wants to know if she can give you an old billy-goat for your birthday," she called.

My exact reply was unprintable!

Anne was still laughing about it when she came off the phone, and so was I.

Alice and her husband, Ian, are well known for their sense of humour, so I thought you might like to hear the story of the goat.

When Ian had gone out to work one morning, he had found the beast in one of his fields near the road. Someone had obviously wanted to see the back of the animal and had turned it loose.

At first Ian and Alice had thought someone would claim it, but they didn't, and Ian said he wasn't surprised. The smell from the animal was unbearable!

Eventually they put an advert in the paper to see if anyone had lost a

goat, but had no response.

Finally Ian rang the police and asked if they would take it into custody for trespassing on his land.

Apparently their answer was the same as mine!

The police were a little more helpful than I had been, though. They told Ian that if no-one had claimed the goat after four weeks, he could sell it.

A cattle man his whole life, Ian says he will never live down the fact that he took a goat to Cupar auction!

But all he was hoping for was that someone would bid and take it off their farm and off their hands!

Well, the bidding began, and Ian was surprised at the interest that wee goat generated.

He was delighted with the price he received – and he was most relieved to see the back of his unwanted guest!

We never did find out where it had come from, but it all ended happily for Ian and for the stray goat.

And Alice had to come up with another idea for my birthday present! ◼

A Moment To Treasure

Perfect weather, perfect food, perfect company. Yes, it was a perfect day . . .

'D never seen a Cheshire cat – until the other day. It was on a beautiful summer's evening. The sun was shining and the Riggin was at peace.

Anne and I were sitting in the summerhouse in easy chairs with our feet up. Her face was wreathed in smiles – like a Cheshire cat.

"John, I've really enjoyed today."

So had I.

"I'm glad they came. Do you think they enjoyed it?"

"If what they ate was anything to go by, they certainly did! They won't want a meal till Wednesday!"

To go back to the beginning . . .

The phone rang one evening and Anne answered. It was our son.

"Could we all come on Sunday for lunch?"

It was his birthday, so you can guess the answer!

"Delighted to see you all. Let's hope it's a fine day. We'll have lunch in the garden."

I'm not a keen gardener, but Anne has always loved it. Unfortunately, neither of us is getting any younger, so she decided to redesign the garden so that it was easier to look after.

She dragged me out one spring evening to see what I thought of her ideas. It was then I got my inspiration – but I kept it to myself.

Anne outlined her ideas – slabs, chips, trees and bushes. I agreed to get someone in to do it.

The men came to dig up the garden, lay slabs and spread chips. I went out to supervise, and told them to lay six slabs one way and four another under the top wall.

Anne asked why, but I wouldn't say.

I was still silent two days later when the lorry arrived. On it were four sides, roof and floor of a summerhouse. They erected it on the slabs. Anne was delighted.

As you know, Anne never does anything by halves. She got me to put up a curtain rail along the back.

Two easy chairs followed, then a table and a piece of carpet. It's all very comfortable!

It was lovely and sunny the morning the family was coming to lunch.

Anne decided to serve the meal in the summerhouse as it's so beautiful out there with the view across the Forth.

So what did we have to eat?

Well, for starters we had herring in a dressing and vinegar with a knob of butter. The children were offered melon as an alternative.

The main course was one of Anne's real steak and kidney pies with mushrooms and a crust. She served it with new potatoes, cabbage and peas.

Finally, raspberries and fresh cream. And don't forget the coffee!

It was a super day – and a super meal.

Long after Anne and I are gone, our grandchildren and their parents will talk about the day they had lunch in Gran's summerhouse. Surely a moment to remember and treasure. ■

Anne likes to offer advice on the sheep.

Friends & Family

Keep In Touch!

We're always delighted when our grandchildren do just that.

H I, Gran!" A cheery young voice greets Anne over the blower. Anne's brain works overtime for about three seconds. Which one of the five is talking? If she gets the wrong one, they don't mind!

I think there are a lot of inventions that mankind could well have done without, but I'd be the first to say thanks to the man who invented the telephone.

Last Sunday evening, three calls from the grandchildren had made Anne's day.

She came back to her Orkney chair and sat staring into space. It was one of those times when it's best to say nothing and just let silence prevail.

When she finally spoke, after what seemed like an eternity, it was just to say, "Bless them!"

She turned towards me and I could see a tear rolling down her cheek.

Anne and I have five grandchildren, ranging in ages from sixteen to twenty-six. Four boys and a girl, and they all think the world of Gran, my dear Anne.

They often call her for a chat because they know they can trust Gran to keep their secrets.

She doesn't even tell me because, as she says, "You can't keep your mouth shut, John."

She knows I can't resist pulling their legs.

Three of them came to her when their love affairs were not going smoothly.

They're lucky. Anne always has a wealth of sound advice to put them right. I think she should write an Agony Aunt column in some magazine.

Yes, they're lucky. I had a Victorian granny and I would never have dared even mention the subjects they discuss with their gran, let alone ask for her advice.

I loved my granny, the dear soul, all dressed up in black to one inch off the floor.

She was straight, honest, owed no-one a penny and went to church twice on Sunday.

But there was none of the easy chat between us that there is between Anne and our lot.

It was a different time and a different generation, I suppose.

Are grannies really so much different these days? Do they all find it easier to discuss life and its problems?

I know Anne feels that she wants our grandchildren to have the benefit of her "experience" – I daren't say "mistakes"!

I know I had no-one to discuss girl problems with until I met Anne. She had siblings and made it easy for me to talk to her. It's a skill she has never lost.

Anne and I have often wondered what our youngest grandchild will do for a living.

When he was very young, he informed Anne he was going into antiques, but I think he's gone off the idea. They have more opportunities than we did, that's for sure.

Oh, well, wherever they all end up, thanks to the genius who invented the telephone, they will always be able to get in touch with their dear gran whenever they need a little bit of advice or encouragement! ■

Helping Round The House

Some men are hopeless round the house — and they're the lucky ones!

HAVE you noticed that the men who don't lift a finger round the house are the ones who generally get away with it? That's how it seems, in my experience.

At one do I was dragged to, to keep her ladyship company, a friend of Anne's remarked, "Oh, Tommy's just hopeless. He couldn't boil an egg."

The poor fellow just sat there.

He smiled, I noted, but said nothing. All those round the table knew he served his wife breakfast on a tray, in bed.

It was only cereal, toast, marmalade and coffee, but my Anne would have to be very ill indeed before she would consider taking breakfast in bed.

I sometimes think he was smarter than he looked. If his wife believed he was useless, she would never ask him to do anything!

Things have to be done the way she likes them, but Anne doesn't mind me helping when she is giving one of her small dinner parties at the Riggin.

"John, be a dear and lay the table."

Isn't it a fiddly do, laying it all out correctly? I say correctly, as one evening a gentleman guest said to his wife in a stage whisper, "Which of these darned things do I use?"

I often wonder what she said to him on the way home. I know what Anne would have said to me!

"Are you having a cloth or mats, dear?"

"Mats, I think, they look nicer. Oh, and John, would you mind giving the table a polish, then? And don't forget the napkins and the napkin rings!"

Anne was having three couples in for supper once — supper, not dinner. I couldn't have told you which was which, myself. We were getting cold fare, not hot — that was the only difference as far as I could see.

I heard her mutter to herself that she was going to make a potato salad.

Later in the day she had slipped into Crail for something from the grocer's — that shop I like that smells of Eastern promise. You get all sorts of tasty bits in there. It has a name — deli-something — but I can't spell it.

I thought I'd make myself useful and help with the potato salad. I went out to the barn, got a bag of potatoes and hunted through it for the wee ones.

When I had a wee bagful I took them into the kitchen, washed them, put them in a pan of cold water and salted them.

Anne came home before they had finished boiling and it was then I realised I should have peeled them.

Fortunately Anne got the skins off once they were cooked, but that didn't stop her telling me what she thought of me all the time she was doing it!

That's what I get for trying to help!

Well, we all make mistakes, don't we? Sometimes I wish I was more of a lost cause around the house.

At least if I was never asked to help I would avoid making a mess of things! ▪

Just Drop In

A simple invitation to visit?
Don't you believe it!

ANNE was out at her hens when the phone rang, so I had to pick it up. Usually answering the blasted thing is something I leave to her.

It was a lady we knew telling us that a farmer friend of ours, Callum, had to go into hospital.

I felt really sorry for Callum. He didn't have anyone to look after him now.

Callum and his wife, Peggy, were the salt of the earth. A finer, more God-fearing couple you couldn't wish to meet.

They had a farm between Crail and Anstruther. Peggy was a farmer's daughter, big, cheerful and hard-working. They were a happy and successful couple – maybe not in terms of money, I don't know, but certainly in everything that matters.

One day, driving back from Cupar, Callum had a car accident. It wasn't serious, but it shook him, and shortly afterwards they decided to retire.

They sold the farm and bought a bonnie house in Pittenweem with a large garden.

They had three happy years together growing flowers and veg and doing their own thing.

Then Peggy fell ill suddenly and three weeks later Callum was left on his own.

As I put the phone down, I wondered who else I could get to go and see Callum.

Then it came to me. Molly would do it. She was a widow, and she had been in my class at school.

So I rang her right away and told her about Callum.

"John, he's asked me to go round a few times, but I've never quite liked to. He said drop in any time — but he never said when."

I ask you, would Callum, or any other farmer, for that matter, think of saying, "Oh, Molly, would you like to come round next Wednesday at quarter to three?"

When he said drop in, he meant just that. Drop in any time for a natter.

How Anne laughed when she came back. She was able to explain it quite logically.

She was, by the way, referring to her town friends.

"John, if they say drop in any time, you know they hope you won't dream of it.

"But if they do mean it, they'll ask you to drop round next Wednesday at four for tea and scones!"

That night, Anne went to see Callum herself. I went mid-morning two days later after I'd been delivering some tatties in Anstruther.

"Oh, John, I'm glad you dropped in."

I could see that he was.

So what I would say is don't wait for someone to give you a date and time when they ask you to visit — just take them at their word and drop in.

You'll undoubtedly brighten their day and bring real happiness to a lonely person. ■

In The Good Books

A Sunday School service took me back to my own prize-winning days!

ANNE and I were spending a weekend with friends of ours, Jo and Ian, on their sheep farm in Perthshire. Up Glen Lyon, you're at peace with nature, or that's how I always feel when I am there.

The River Lyon runs through the bottom fields whilst the ground rises steeply from the valley.

There's trout in the river and plovers, snipe and oyster-catchers to watch and listen to in the valley.

I always enjoy our visits and it's nice to get a wee change of scene.

On the Sunday we always go to the morning service in their wee church.

"It'll be a children's service as it's the Sunday School prize-giving. I hope you don't mind," Jo said.

Of course we didn't. In fact, I think Anne would agree with me when I say that we enjoyed it more than an adult Sunday service.

There were five children in all, aged between five and nine.

The minister had brought a compass to church and, as it couldn't be seen from their seats, all five bairns went forward and sat with the minister on the step up to the communion table.

He was very good with them and they really enjoyed finding north, south, east and west.

That scene of five children and the minister sitting in a circle is one that Anne and I will remember for the rest of our lives.

To each of the four eldest, the minister handed a large card on which he had drawn the letters *N*, *S*, *E*, *W*.

He arranged it so that when they stood up to show us the letters, they spelled the word *NEWS*. From there he developed his children's address which they listened to very attentively.

Anne remarked later that they would probably remember it all their days.

It was the next part of the service that prompted me to tell you about that weekend — the actual prize-giving, when the children received their books.

When I looked at Anne, I could see she was having a job not to shed a tear, as it brought back memories of the days when our bairns stepped up to collect their prizes.

Time goes so fast when your children are small. It didn't seem all that long ago that I was getting my Sunday school prizes, never mind our bairns!

They say great minds think alike.

Without a word to each other Anne and I both went in search of our Sunday school prize books when we got back to the Riggin after our lovely wee holiday up Glen Lyon.

I found my first one, which was looking a bit worse for wear. Little wonder, I suppose, as the date was 1921!

Anne found one of hers, a well-thumbed copy of the classic "Little Women".

In the end we came across quite a few and each one brought back memories of childhood and Sunday school, and of trying not to miss a Sunday so the inscription on the book would read, *For Perfect Attendance*.

I'm glad we went to Jo and Ian's for the weekend. It was a refreshing change, full of moments to treasure. ▪

All I Want For Christmas . . .

Anne might not approve, but I know what I want from Santa this year . . .

IT was about twelve noon on a Friday and Anne and I had just finished lunch when that infernal machine — reputed to give so much happiness — rang.

Anne and our Mary chatted for twenty minutes. I timed them by the kitchen clock.

"That was Mary."

As if I didn't know.

"She wants to know what you want for Christmas. You've to ring her back on Sunday."

I would have loved to have said, "Peace and no harrassment from my family." But I didn't.

I know it's difficult to think of what to get the "old man". Don't get me wrong — at my age, I've got nearly everything I want.

In the past, Anne and I used to have the same trouble with my parents. Once, I sent Dad a shaving brush, as he, like me, didn't like the electric ones.

He wrote and thanked me, and said he'd put it with with the other brushes he had been given.

When Anne and I cleared out his house after he died, we found fifteen pristine, never-used shaving brushes!

My mother was even more difficult. She was a stickler for birthdays and I was never much good at remembering the dates.

One year, Anne, at great expense, bought Mum a beautiful mohair wrap. It was a lovely piece of workmanship and the colours were out of this world. We both wished it was ours.

It came back with a curt note. *I'm not in my dotage yet. I don't need a rug around my shoulders.*

Another year, we wrapped some perfume in a Harrods bag we happened to have in the house. That did the trick.

How nice of you to go to all that trouble to get perfume sent from Harrods.

My foot! That perfume was bought in Perth! We just decided to increase its value by one hundred per cent. by putting it in a Harrods bag. Can't folk be taken in?

So what should I tell Mary on Sunday? I consulted Anne.

"A shirt?"

Well, I have four brand new shirts in the cupboard.

"Pyjamas, then?"

How exciting!

Did I ever tell you about what Anne did one year when she was stuck for a present for me? When we woke up, she wished me a merry Christmas and told me my present was in the lounge.

I pottered downstairs but could see no parcel, large or small.

It was a new rug for the fireplace! Some Christmas present!

Now, our son gives me "The Countryman" for one of my presents. I enjoy reading it — and the notion set me thinking.

On the Sunday, I said to Mary that I knew of a publisher in Devon who printed books about the countryside. Would she like to take it from there?

Anne didn't agree with my choice. She thought I should have asked for something useful and practical.

But I enjoy reading! And, if you think about it, men might not be such a problem when it comes to Christmas if you think what he'd really like — not what you think he should have! ▪

Every Picture Tells A Story

I was looking for inspiration, but I ended up on a trip down memory lane!

THE other evening I was sitting at my desk in my office with a blank pad in front of me. I had an idea of what I wanted to tell you, but I was determined to get my facts right.

I went over to the huge wardrobe to try to find a file. Anne says I'm like a magpie because I hoard everything, but where's the harm?

During my search, I came across a file of old photographs. This distracted me for so long that eventually Anne came in to check that I was still alive!

"Look at that, dear." I handed her a tattered, brown photo. It was taken in

1935, the first picture I ever took of my dear Anne.

How we laughed. Anne had her hair in earphones and was wearing a brown dress with spots. I thought she looked beautiful.

We spent the rest of the evening looking through the snaps.

There was one of me when I was around seven, sitting on the back of a huge Clydesdale.

Another picture was of Anne's mother and father and her sisters in a hay field. The girls wore dresses which touched the ground and a hay cart stood in the background.

Anne handed me a sepia photo which made me smile. It was a studio photo of Great-granny, Great-grandpa and their three girls and one boy. They looked like waxwork models, and not a smile in sight.

The women wore dresses down to the ground and the men suffered in high starched collars. Nineteen-year-old Aunt Isabella looked forty if she was a day!

I must admit we thoroughly enjoyed that evening looking through old photos. And there was one blessing — as I was often the one taking the pictures, there weren't many of me!

Happy memories of days we will never have again, but great to look back upon all the same.

You'll have guessed by this time that my blank sheet of paper remained that way. Oh, well, tomorrow's another day! ■

A Knotty Problem

I hate ties. And I've found a great way of keeping down my stock!

D O you remember these sepia photos of Great-grandad dressed in those high, stiff collars? They must have been murder to wear — and all to be in fashion.

Clothes tend to be far more sensible these days. But there's still one article I hate wearing, and that's a tie.

I have lots and I don't think I paid for one!

A while back, on Anne's instructions, I was trying to sort them out — which to send to the church sale, which to bin and which to keep.

There were several really flamboyant efforts, wide and colourfully patterned.

"See if any of the boys would like them," Anne suggested.

I asked them the next time they paid a visit.

All agreed they wouldn't be seen dead in any of them.

"Grandad," said number one grandson, "I'll give you five pounds if you wear that to church tomorrow."

He held up the most flamboyant tie of all. I didn't go to church in that creation, so he kept his fiver.

As I was going through the collection, though, I came across a real beauty. It was pure silk, in autumn colours — the right shade and design for a man of my age.

I put the tie on. It ran and knotted nicely, and I decided that if I had to wear a tie, that was the one.

I'm not one for bothering about what I wear as long as it keeps me warm.

Anne bought me a thick, woollen jersey for Christmas. I've really taken to it, but it has a fault — it's white. If you lean over a farm gate, it leaves an imprint.

The reason I like it, though, is because I can wear an open shirt underneath and pull the collar out and look quite smart — for me that is.

As you know, I'm not one of these thin fellows — I have a comfortable figure which

Anne is always trying to reduce.

Coming back to the tie business, I now have the answer to the question, "What would you like for Christmas?"

"A silk tie, please."

That sets them back a good twenty pounds or so and they don't ask the same thing the following year, that's for sure.

I get three hankies and some favourite sweets, and my tie collection is thankfully kept in check! ■

The White Stuff

I managed to solve a drink problem with a nice glass of milk!

WE often go to Perth to meet our family from up north — our daughter, Mary, plus son-in-law and children.

Last time, we went looking for a cup of tea and a scone. We found ourselves in a very posh place. I could tell it was posh because the curtains, wallpaper and chair covers all matched!

To everyone's amazement, I ordered a glass of ice-cold milk.

"Milk, Grandad? Are you all right?"

I was, and said so.

In fact, I have been drinking a lot of milk recently as an alternative to tea and coffee, and I really enjoy it.

Talking of drink, it reminds me of a certain occasion in my childhood . . .

My dad was worried — something to do with the farm.

"I think I'll go over and see Tom about it," he said.

"John, you're not fit," my mother protested. But Dad insisted on going, despite a bad cold. Thank goodness he walked!

When Dad went into Tom's kitchen, he was coughing badly.

"John, you need something for that cold," Tom said, and poured him half a glass of malt whisky.

"Now get that down you."

So Dad did, not knowing it was whisky — he was a strict teetotaller.

He immediately felt better, which was hardly surprising! But when he got out into the open air, everything began to swim around. He used fences and walls to help him get home.

Mother, bless her, wanted to send for the doctor, but Dad said no. Just as well!

I've always wondered what Mum said to Tom the next time she met him!

Anne is as good as teetotal, too. She will sometimes take a sherry — "just a wee one, please" — or a glass of white wine. She says red wine is too rich for her.

One evening, all dressed up, we went to a party at the home of one of the bridge girls. I say girls, but I'm being polite — not one of them would see fifty again!

The man of the house asked the first guest what she would like to drink.

"Gin and tonic, please."
He turned to the next.
"A brandy, please."
He gulped, and disappeared into the kitchen.

I watched with amusement. Was he nipping up to the bathroom cabinet for the medicinal brandy, or would he pop out to the off licence?

Neither! He came out of the kitchen and apologised, saying they were out of brandy at the moment.

I learned a lesson that night. Always put your drinks out beforehand, and then tell your guests what you have before asking what they would like!

I suppose we always could offer them a glass of cold milk, couldn't we? ■

It's Good To Talk!

It's amazing what can be accomplished through a chat with an old friend.

THE phone rang just after nine o'clock one morning, and for a change it was for me. It was a fellow farmer, named Jim, a man about half my age.

"John, can we meet and have a blether?"

"Of course — come here."

"No, no — away from the womenfolk."

We agreed to meet in my top field at the big rock.

Anne was disapproving.

"You men shouldn't waste time just blethering. Blethering doesn't bring in the bawbees."

That didn't worry me as much as the fact that Jim was asking the advice of an old man like me.

Of course, I thought the worst. He was a tenant farmer — was there a problem there?

Was the bank pressing him about an overdraft?

I certainly hoped I could help. Jim was a fine lad, with a good wife, a son and two daughters.

We discussed the view, then the state of farming, and at last he got down to his problem.

His son, Gavin, was in his last year at school and didn't want to be a farmer. Jim took his side as he saw no future in farming now.

But his mother, Alice — a farmer's daughter — couldn't think of anything else but farming. It had been good enough for her grandfather, her father and now Jim. Why wasn't it good enough for Gavin?

Anne and I hadn't been faced with this problem. Our son had decided at an early age that he wanted to be an accountant.

"What does Gavin want to do?" I asked.

It was difficult to advise without knowing whether the laddie wanted an open-air job or a desk job. Did he want to be his own boss? Or was he happy enough to work for a wage?

Jim didn't think Gavin would want to be the boss of his own business with lots of men on the payroll. He'd probably want a job in the open air, at least to begin with.

Gavin himself paid me a visit the next day and I was surprised how much homework the young lad had done. He did want an outside job, with the chance of promotion, so we discussed his options.

I learned later that he had gone to university and joined the Forestry Commission.

I'll watch his progress with interest, because I like to think, in some small way, I helped him on his way to his goal.

83

John and Anne enjoy a walk by the waterside.

Out & About

Shall We Go Back?

It was a wonderful holiday.
But we decided it wouldn't be
the same a second time . . .

DO you ever feel you should do something again before it's too late? I know I do.

Then I think, maybe not. That's because, over the years, I've found that when you go back somewhere a second time, the wonder has somehow disappeared.

In any case, I'd have to get our passports renewed!

I found our passports the other night while I was looking for something else.

"Do you think we should get them renewed?" I asked Anne.

"Not with these photos!" she replied.

How the Customs people recognised us I'll never know. Anne had a queer hairdo and I looked like a criminal!

About forty of us had booked through a farming magazine to go on a trip to Lucerne when we got those passports.

We took a boat trip where the guide told us all about the beautiful houses on the lakeside.

We also had a number of hair-raising trips up the mountains in cable cars . . .

"Anne, when did we go to Lucerne?"

"A long time ago, dear."

Can't women be awkward sometimes?

Finally, we agreed that it must have been about twenty-five years ago.

At dinner one evening, we were all given a free ticket for a drink at a local tavern. We all went along.

There was a band playing with a lady singing. I remember thinking she was rather good. As soon as she saw us, she started singing songs in English.

It was a jolly evening, but not really our cup of tea — or should I say, glass of beer! I know we're odd, but you get that way, stuck on your own in the country.

"Like to go for a walk?"

Anne gave my arm a squeeze.

We slipped out and wandered about Lucerne in the moonlight. It was lovely — just the two of us.

Then we went over the bridge and got lost! By the time we found our way again, it was quite late, and everyone was back at the hotel before us!

I have a photo taken on that bridge. Anne is wearing a blue and white spotted dress, standing in front of a hanging basket.

As I said, I'd love to go back. But somehow I don't think we could catch the magic again of walking hand-in-hand over that wooden bridge.

Let's just dream about it . . . ▪

Getting
The Picture

**The old painting is one of our most
treasured possessions. But who will
treasure them when we've gone?**

A **FEW** years ago, Anne and I were visiting her relations in Kirkby Lonsdale. Both of us are drawn to antique shops like bees to honey, so it was no surprise that we ended up looking round one when we went into the town one day.

I found a beautiful watercolour of a local church and bought it for fifteen pounds.

I must get round to putting someone's name on the back of it — otherwise, when we're gone, it will get sold for a few pounds along with our hard-earned, much-loved furniture.

But whose name?

One of Anne's nieces lived in Kirkby Lonsdale, so I'm guessing she might like it.

Yes, I'll put her name on the back. Family squabbles over who gets what might be avoided if we sort it out now!

Anne and I bought bits of furniture to make our house a home, even before we were wed.

One Friday evening, Mother and Dad had gone to attend an auction in Ladybank, and Mother had taken a fancy to an old oak settle that was there.

I'll never forget the row that they had when they got home because each had been waiting for the other to start bidding!

The oak settle had eventually been knocked down to a dealer from St Andrews.

I met Anne in Cupar the following Tuesday and over a cup of tea and a scone in Elder's café, I told her about the settle.

I decided to go home by St Andrews and see if Mr Foster had bought it.

Sure enough, there it was at the back of his shop.

I could see why Mother had wanted it — it was beautiful.

I asked the price with bated breath.

"Five pounds," was the reply.

That was out of our reach.

I asked Mr Foster if he could keep it for three days until I spoke to Anne.

"Let's buy it, John," she said, when I told her. "I'll put in half of the money."

We went back to see Mr Foster, and Anne persuaded him to reduce the price by her bus fare to St Andrews plus another ten shillings if she would pick it up.

We've laughed about it over the years. If we had quarrelled and not got wed, who would have owned the settle?

But, of course, we did get married and we still have the settle.

The problem is now whose name do we put on the back? I wish I knew! ■

A Capital Day Out

London was a far cry from the Riggin, but we still went in search of a good farmhouse breakfast!

I REMEMBER the time, many years ago, when Anne and I took a trip to see Holland's bulb fields. We caught the sleeper from Leuchars to London and laughed and laughed when we saw our little bunk beds — we're used to a king-sized bed!

Ten past seven saw two tired folk getting off the train at King's Cross. We weren't due to leave for Holland until six in the evening, so we had all day to look round London.

All I wanted was a good breakfast!

We joined a long queue for a taxi, and I asked the cabbie to drop us somewhere we could get a good farmhouse breakfast.

He dropped us at Johnny Lyons Corner House near Trafalgar Square. It was packed, and to give Johnny his due, we enjoyed a real farmhouse breakfast — bacon, sausage, egg, a piece of black pudding and a few mushrooms, plus steaming coffee and no washing up.

Suitably replete, we headed for Trafalgar Square and St Martin-in-the-Fields.

"John, I'd like to go to Fortnum and Mason's," Anne announced, so we walked there.

I was really taken with the men in frock coats and the display of things for sale.

"John, could we go to Harrod's?" was Anne's next request.

We took a taxi. I'm no mole, so the idea of travelling on those underground trains didn't appeal to me.

In the afternoon, after a pub lunch, we went to see Westminster Abbey and the Houses of Parliament, then a taxi took us to St Paul's. We couldn't help wondering how they got that dome in place without the modern technology available to today's builders.

That night on the Channel boat we slept the sleep of the just until we were wakened at 5.00 a.m. But Anne had enjoyed her day seeing the sights in London, and that was all I cared about.

A moment in time, but a very happy day far from the Riggin. ■

To Cap It All

If you want to get ahead, get a hat!

Do you ever get a desire to do something? I do.

I'll never forget when I met the husband of one of Anne's bridge friends in Cupar one August. He and his wife had just got back from two weeks in Tenerife.

"John, where have you and Anne been for your holidays?"

Well, Anne and I had been in St Monans for an afternoon to a funeral at the famous church by the sea. It was a beautiful day. We strolled down to the harbour after the funeral to watch the boats bobbing about in the water.

Anne made one of those classic remarks:

"John, if I go first, find the key for the front door. It's on top of the grandfather clock. I've never been out of our front door, so it would be my last chance. If you go first, I'll do it for you."

To be honest, I was feeling hale and hearty till then and I couldn't care less whether I go out the back or front door!

Anyway, I've rambled from my desire.

I think I told you, a few years back, that Anne once made me buy a bowler hat after going with me to Anstruther cemetery to a lady's funeral.

On the way home, Anne insisted that she wasn't having me go to another funeral in a cap. I had to get a bowler.

Well, I didn't know that you shouldn't go into a shop and say, "My size is seven and seven-eighths." Oh, no, there's a ritual about buying and fitting a bowler.

Anne found out I could get one fitted at Forsyth's in Princes Street, Edinburgh.

The gent – a wee gent – just on the left as you entered that famous store (now no more) fitted a kind of typewriter thing on my head. It cut a paper pattern of my head's shape. If you have ever seen a plover's egg – narrow at one end and wide at the other – well, that was the shape of my head.

When we went back to collect the bowler, it had been steamed and shaped . . . yes, and looked just like a large plover's egg.

Well, that must have been over 30 years ago. I enjoyed my bowler. It fitted like a glove, if you know what I mean! It never blew off and there was more elegance in lifting it off and saying to one of Anne's posh bridge pals, "Good morning to you."

Anyway, I hadn't worn it for years when I got it down off a top shelf in the bedroom and plonked it on my head.

Had it shrunk or had my head swelled? It must have been the latter. Whichever, it sat like a wart on the back end of a pig! How Anne laughed. There and then I got a desire to buy a new bowler.

Our daughter, Mary, and her husband, Anne and I, all went to Edinburgh to a carol service at school at Christmas.

The ladies asked if they could have five minutes in Jenners. I knew they would be at least half an hour, so once we had found one of those expensive stables for the car, I set off in quest of one bowler.

Dunns, the hatters – "No, sorry."

Jenners – "No, try Cunningham, St Andrews Square."

When I got there, a dear soul was trying to pick the right size and colour of braces for her son.

"Madam, do you mind if I ask Mr Cunningham a question?"

"Oh, no."

"Do you sell bowlers, sir?"

"Yes."

"About how much do they cost now?"

"From fifty-five pounds."

I don't remember seeing a chair I could sit on, so I said, "Thank you, I'll be back."

Anne and Mary were still taking coffee and cakes in Jenners when I flopped down into a seat beside them.

I would still like a bowler. I wonder if Anne will go 50-50 with me for my birthday? ▪

Putting On The Style!

In my humble opinion, my Anne puts all the other ladies in the shade!

THE Perth Bull Sales is far more than just a sale of bulls. It is a major event in the social calendar of farmers' wives.

A few may be genuinely interested in the livestock, but it's always been my opinion that the women are more interested in each other's attire.

It may not be Royal Ascot, but it is quite a stylish affair.

We don't go every year as I don't keep a stock bull any more, but last year Anne said she'd like to go anyway.

I agreed, on the condition that I could take her out for lunch.

For once Anne didn't get into a flap about what to wear.

Usually, she spends endless nights trying on her entire wardrobe and accosting me around the house to ask, "What do you think of this?" and then ignore my answer!

I'm afraid I'm not much help — as far as I'm concerned, she's a credit to the Riggin no matter what she wears.

I'm not good at describing what women wear. Anne says I'm hopeless. But I do remember clearly what Anne was wearing that particular day.

It was a very attractive heather-coloured top and matching skirt with a real topper of a blouse underneath.

The whole outfit was very smart indeed and Anne looked extremely elegant.

But it was her hat, her crowning glory, which really impressed me. Anne had it made specially years ago, and it suits her as well now as it did then.

I'll never forget the formal and polite assistant saying, "An ideal hat for going to market, madam."

Well, I couldn't see Anne sporting that creation at Cupar Market, but obviously the Bull Sales was the right and proper place for such a masterpiece.

We went for lunch in a hotel overlooking the Tay.

Since Anne can cook beef and lamb better than anyone, I went for prawns in rather a rich, creamy sauce served with noodles.

When the waitress put a fork and a spoon in front of me, I feared the worst.

It was a very interesting dish, but I just couldn't cope with the noodles.

There was only one thing for it.

"A knife, please," I said to the waitress.

I cut the noodles up into wee pieces and enjoyed them very much.

Anne kept well away from more exotic dishes and had a salad instead.

But she said she'd really enjoyed herself at lunch — especially watching me trying to eat mine! ■

Sweets For My Sweet . . .

Perhaps these weren't Anne's exact words to me — but I still insist she can make a mean pudding!

I'M in trouble again, because in Anne's opinion I have no imagination. It all started when we were asked out to join some friends who'd come to St Andrews from New Zealand. They'd invited us out to dinner.

It was all because of my action — or lack of action — at the pudding stage that I'm in trouble.

"What wonderful puddings!" I murmured, as the trolley rolled up to our table.

Anne gave me a look.

"John, you are hopeless," she said, in a tone to turn the cream sour. "They're not called puddings now. They're sweets."

Fair enough. I knew better than to argue. So I looked at the sweet trolley. There were all sorts of wonderful concoctions.

I must tell you, before I forget, about the time Anne and I went out for dinner and I decided to have what looked like two halves of hard-boiled egg, but much bigger, stuck together with cream.

Anne never warned me about my choice. When I tried to take a spoonful it flew right off the table.

"John, go and pick it up," she whispered, looking embarrassed.

"You must be joking," I replied.

Well, I ask you — would you have done it?

Nowadays I play safe and ask for biscuits and cheese, and heaven help them if it's not a good selection!

I like to see a lot of cheeses, tomatoes and celery, plus a basket full of biscuits and butter. Anne says it's no wonder I'm eighteen stone.

Well, the night our friends took us out, the girl brought the sweet trolley, and I must say, someone had gone to a lot of trouble to create that mouthwatering array.

I noticed some small creme caramels and, when my turn came, I asked for two.

"Cream, sir?"

"Yes, please."

Anne gave me a glare.

Well, we do produce milk, and we have to support home industries.

I enjoyed that caramel so much that when I was next in Crail I bought two packets.

Once home, I read the instructions, and they appeared so simple that any fool, even John Taylor, could make them.

However, given my cooking history, I plucked up my courage and asked Anne to make it.

To her credit, she produced the goods without even looking at the instructions. The end result was beautiful.

You can keep your pudding trolley — ordinary creme caramels and biscuits and cheese will do me! ■

Decisions, Decisions . . .

The Taylors are running late, and for once it's not my fault!

AT lunchtime on Wednesday, the phone rang. Anne went to answer it.

"John and I would be delighted to come, Mabel. We won't be late. Thanks, Mabel."

She came back to the table.

"That was Mabel."

I refrained from making a sarcastic comment.

"She wants us for dinner a week on Saturday, and we haven't to be late."

"Why?"

"She doesn't want the dinner to spoil while she's waiting for latecomers."

As it was two weeks away, I suggested to Anne that she decide in the next few days what she was going to wear.

She suggested I have a haircut.

I came in earlier than usual on the Saturday of the dinner. Anne was fluttering about the bedroom.

"John, shall I wear this?"

Now, I ask you. She had had two weeks to decide, and at the eleventh hour she was asking for my advice.

"Yes, I like that, dear."

I had bought her that outfit when we were in Perth for the Bull Sales.

"But I've lost weight since then. It doesn't hang properly on me now." Anne disappeared.

"Isn't that more like me, dear?" She appeared in a long dress.

"No, dear. It's too long and too tight."

Anne went away in a huff.

"Anne," I called, "you said Mabel wanted us there at seven-thirty."

She promptly reappeared in another long dress.

"Just the ticket, dear."

My granddaughter once told me that I wouldn't get to heaven if I swore. If Anne had taken much longer, I would definitely have been off St Peter's list!

It was ten past seven and Mabel's farm was twenty minutes away, flat out.

"Will I call Mabel and tell her we'll be late?"

Guess what? Anne's not going to heaven either!

We eventually got on our way, but we were still fifteen minutes late. Anne apologised profusely and handed over a pot of marmalade, which was a bit like taking coals to Newcastle — that's what Mabel always brings us when she visits!

But despite our late arrival, the dinner was one to savour — roast beef, a trifle and biscuits and cheese.

And Anne looked delightful in her third choice of evening dress! ■

A Recipe For Happiness!

I don't think anything can cheer you up like some good home-baking — especially Anne's.

ANNE'S odd sometimes.

I don't mean not the full shilling, not by any means. She's the full shilling and then some. And, as I've often told you, she's a great baker and cook.

If someone's coming to see her for something to do with one of her many worthy causes, she always says, "Drop in about three" and prepares one of her splendid afternoon teas: sandwiches, cake and scones.

Anne's a real expert with scones — plain, sultana, cheese or treacle. When they are filled with butter, they're out of this world.

Now, why did I start out by saying Anne was odd?

Well, I came in for lunch one Wednesday recently. It was a foul day. The wind was blowing straight from Siberia, or wherever the next landfall is after Fife Ness.

"John, you're invited to tea at Jessie's."

Jessie is a widow who lives in Crail. I would say she's around seventy, but Anne says she's much older. She's one of those sparrow-like old ladies, full of vitality.

Anne had been on the phone to her and had thought she sounded a little lonely, so when Jessie asked us to come for tea, she accepted at once.

When we arrived, we found Jessie had been busy, and she was happy at having something to occupy her. She had made scones and a fruitcake.

The scones weren't the same as any that Anne makes, but she couldn't work out what was different about them.

"Jessie, your scones are beautiful. You will give me the recipe, won't you?"

Jessie told her she had never used a recipe, but she said she would try to write it down.

This is why I said earlier that Anne was odd. She can make every type of scone known to man, and here she was asking for yet another recipe.

On the way home, I asked her about it. Her answer was quite sensible.

"It pleased Jessie that I wanted her recipe — and I wanted to try them for myself."

Jessie wrote out the recipe and it went into the folder at home with about a hundred others!

A few days later, Anne decided to make some chocolate fudge for our grandsons, who are doing for themselves away at university. Anne is convinced they won't be getting enough to eat.

The recipe was in a favourite cookbook of mine: "Orkney Island Recipes".

It's one of my favourites because there is a fantastic chapter about home-brewed ale, which ends like this:

Store the full bottles like precious ingots and be patient for at least a fortnight. Then, some despicable evening, blow up the fire, open a couple of bottles, sip, swallow, and behold the squandering in defeat of many of the miseries of this world.

I've often thought this was rather well-put — but, you know, I can get the same feeling of wellbeing tucking into a few of Anne's warm scones with lots and lots of butter! ■

It's A Date!

On special occasions, I always use my dress sense and please myself!

"J OHN, you must wear a suit."

This is one of Anne's standard orders if we're going out for the evening with some of her bridge friends from St Andrews. I've no idea why. But if all the other men in the party are wearing them, I suppose I must conform.

I had to smile one particular evening when Anne appeared in a long dress. I made no comment other than, "You look bonnie tonight, dear."

When we arrived, I couldn't help noticing that the other three ladies, plus hostess, all sported long frocks.

I'm not daft, and quickly came to the conclusion that there had been an increase in our phone bill that day.

I tackled Anne as we were going home. I was right. "The girls" had rung each other and decided it would be nice to give their long dresses an airing.

The other week,

Anne had received a call from Marie, another farmer's wife. The outcome of that long conversation was, "Yes, we'll be delighted to come — what time?"

Then she turned to me.

"John, we're going to Marie's tonight for a bite."

I had no objections as Ian, the husband, and I get on well. But there was one other thing to be sorted out.

The minute Anne went outside to feed her hens, I did her telephone trick.

"Ian, you're not wearing a suit tonight, are you? For goodness' sake don't dress up, or I'll be in trouble."

That evening I put on an open-necked shirt and grey flannels.

"John, you can't go out looking like that! Ian will be wearing a suit!" Anne protested.

I dug my heels in. If I couldn't dress casually for a night at a friend's, there was something far wrong.

Anne hardly spoke a word to me as we drove the three miles to their farm.

But when we arrived, there was Ian, in flannels, no tie, and a pullover which had, even to my eyes, seen better days.

On the way home I was sorely tempted to comment on Ian's attire, but there are times when silence is golden — and I reckoned this was one of them.

Funnily enough, Anne's bridge friends are getting older at the same rate we are! As a result, there's not as many invitations to dinner for which I have to dress, thank goodness. They seem to have mostly been replaced by, "Come over for a bite to eat."

The date is often that night, or no more than three days away.

I'm told by Anne, the etiquette expert, that you were supposed to give six weeks' notice so that you could enter it in your engagement diary!

I had to laugh. Ours is a big calendar hung up in the kitchen. Nowadays it notes WRI meetings, my rather infrequent visits to the NFU and not much else.

However, it reminds me that the Farmers' Ball in Cupar is coming up soon, so I'll have to look out my penguin suit, shake out the moths and live in hope that the trousers will still meet around my waist. I've already had one gusset put in at the back. I don't think I could have another.

Anne, I'm sure, will look as lovely as she always does. But if I comment on her appearance, no doubt her reply will be, "John, I've had this outfit for over fifteen years!"

And what can I say to that except, "Darling, it looks as good as new."

A very careful sort, my Anne, but I'm mighty proud of her. ▪

Under Lock And Key

Keys are the bane of my life – I can never remember where I've left them!

WE'VE reached a sorry state of affairs. That's the conclusion I've come to.

I was sitting in the buggy outside St Andrews post office, waiting for my Anne. She was posting a letter to our eldest grandson, who was in Canada for six weeks. Anne was worried he'd be lonely, but personally I have my doubts.

Anyway, there was a long queue, so I had lots of time to sit and watch the world go by. Three people on cycles appeared, and before going into the post office each one of them chained their bike to a lamppost.

What a sad state of affairs if you can't leave your cycle unattended for five minutes while you go into a shop. To be honest, it really made my blood boil.

Has the meaning of honesty gone for ever?

I know that neither Anne nor myself would ever dream of picking up something which wasn't ours. And it's not something we were specially taught, we just knew you didn't do it.

When I was young, I don't remember us ever locking the back door. Now, if we go anywhere, the back door is locked securely and, if it's Anne going out, the key is left in a suitable place.

Keys are the bane of our lives.

"Where are the car keys? Have you seen the garage key? Where's the back door key?"

Oh, for the days when we never had to lock anything because we trusted everyone.

Thinking about old-fashioned keys, I suppose some readers may remember when I was dragged by Anne to a wedding in Kirkby Lonsdale.

We stayed at the hotel in the square. At that time, many moons ago, the hotel was full of antiques.

Anne was really taken by the owner's ideas of making simple things pleasing to the eye.

Just as we entered from the cobbled courtyard, there were lots of keys hanging on the wall in a simple design. Anne was intrigued.

All someone had done was to get seven large keys, six smaller, then five and down to the bottom with a very wee key. A triangle of keys, in other words, from big to small.

When we went home, Anne searched for her own collection of keys.

Anne says she's the one who knows her antiques, and she says those types of keys are valuable collectors' pieces.

But they're no good to me unless they open my back door! ■

Poppies in bloom in abundance on the Riggin of Fife.

In Anne's Kitchen

The Spice Of Life!

Eggs, fish, rice and curry powder — it could all add up to a recipe for disaster!

HAD been at a sale in the Tay valley, and I decided to drop in on our daughter, Mary, on the way home. She gave me a warm welcome and asked if I had had any lunch.

When I said no, she gave me a lecture on eating properly. I laughed. Her mother would have said that missing a meal was the best thing for me!

"If I'd known you were coming I'd have done a roast," Mary said. "Would a kedgeree do?"

I didn't know what that was, but I'll try anything once.

I watched with interest as rice went into a pan. Smoked haddock came out of the freezer and was cooked in milk then mashed up.

Mary shelled two hard-boiled eggs and cut them up, then all the ingredients were mixed together, turned into a dish, and put into the Aga.

We chatted while she set the table. I was pleased to see she had put out a big chunk of cheese and a basket of biscuits.

Whatever Mary called that fish dish, it was really good, and I told Anne about my tasty lunch when I got home.

"John, I could knock you up one of those any time."

Anne's "any time" is one of these elastic terms. It never happens.

A week or so later, Anne was out for the evening at the WRI, so I made my plans. I had bought two pieces of smoked haddock when the fish van had come round.

As soon as the back door closed behind Anne, I started to make my kedgeree.

I put three eggs in a pan to boil, and the fish in a pan with milk. How was I to know it would boil over if I didn't watch it?

Then I put the rice in a pan with water and added salt.

Now this is where it all started to go wrong. I went over to check on a cow that was about to calf, and I stayed too long.

How was I to know the water in the rice would evaporate? The fish was overcooked but, thank goodness, there was still water in the bottom of the egg pan.

I managed to rescue everything and assemble it the way I had seen Mary do. Then I decided to add some curry powder to perk it up a bit. Anne says I would add curry and onions to anything!

When Anne came home, all the pans were washed and away.

"John, what's that odd smell?"

She went over to the oven and burst out laughing.

"I can't turn my back but you're thinking of your tummy!"

We both enjoyed that kedgeree and, to my mind, it was even better than Mary's — thanks to the curry powder. ▪

Out Of The Frying-pan

I don't think there is anything quite as nice as the smell of fried onions. Unfortunately for me, Anne doesn't agree!

IN our early days on the Riggin, the calves were Anne's responsibility. She had real patience with them, and could bring them on better than I ever could. I always valued her opinion where they were concerned.

I was in the calf shed one morning and I needed her advice about something, so, seeing her crossing the yard, I decided to give her a shout.

"What is it, John? I've got the dinner on!"

She came over, though. Anne can never resist a chance to get "hands-on" with the stock – especially if she thinks she can do it better than me!

She gave me the answer to my question, then spent a little while passing an opinion on each of the calves until she remembered the dinner.

She flew across the yard like the dogs were after her and threw open the back door.

Black smoke came out in clouds, and the smell almost knocked me over.

Anne had been frying sausages, liver and onions. A few more minutes and the whole place would have gone up in flames.

I have to say I was disappointed. I knew I'd be lucky to get a cold cheese sandwich now.

I kept well away from the house for the rest of the afternoon, but when I did venture back, I noted that the curtains had already been washed and the carpet and rugs were out on the green.

Jim, the lad, was beating the carpet. As soon as I saw that I wondered what I would be press-ganged into doing.

My Anne's a great one for action – today, not tomorrow. When she decides something needs done, it gets done – not always by Anne herself, though.

That lingering smell of onions had to be got rid of before the day was out, so I was set to wash the walls above the height that Anne couldn't reach herself. She made sure that I washed out the cloth every few yards.

"John, if a job's worth doing, it's worth doing well."

I had my own thoughts on whether it was worth doing at all, but I kept my mouth shut.

The ceiling, the tops of all the cupboards, the light fitting and the tops of all the doors had to be washed and polished, with her ladyship in attendance like Brittania to see I didn't shirk my task.

By night-time, I was wet to the elbows and like a limp rag, but the kitchen and the living-room smelled of soap.

Personally, I preferred the smell of onions, but there's no accounting for taste! ▪

A Trying Time

I'm making an effort to eat more sensibly, stop smoking and exercise. These are trying times and no mistake!

ANNE, as you know, is a very good cook. She says that's why I married her, but that's not true — she was a very good stock girl, too!

In recent years, I've tried to cut down a bit. I've cut out the big bowl of porridge and fry-up for breakfast, but by lunchtime I'm ready for a square meal.

Anne tries to grill instead of fry and I have noticed more salads creeping in at teatime — Anne says they're good for me.

I get peckish about ten when we're thinking of climbing the stairs. I've tried to overrule my desire for a thick cheese sandwich, but it's difficult — although I do think I sleep better without the cheese, though I'd never admit that to Anne.

Anne has been buying more fruit lately — oranges, apples and bananas, as she says they're good for me, too. Something to do with fibre, I think.

I must admit, recently I've got into the habit of choosing something out of her fruit bowl as I pass, and eating it while I'm working about the farm.

I decided — quite sensibly for me — that it was no use making such an effort to eat healthily if I was still going to continue to smoke too much!

So I am trying to give that up, too, but it's easier said than done!

I did it once before, years ago. I was in bed with flu and I felt so awful I couldn't think of smoking.

I didn't smoke for three days, so I just didn't start again.

But then, a few years ago, Anne was in hospital and I was very worried. A farmer friend rang to ask after her and I told him my concerns.

"John, you used to smoke. Start again — it'll help your nerves," he advised.

Well, I was in such a state about Anne that it sounded like a good idea.

Like a fool, I did what he said, and have been back on the pipe ever since.

Now, though, I really have resolved to stop. But the second day, I was in such agony that I struck a compromise.

It was too hard to cut it out completely, so, to begin with, I decided I wouldn't pick up my pipe till nine o'clock in the evening.

Well, that's where I am now, and I'm quite determined I'm going to stick to it until I can bring myself to leave my pipe on its rack for ever more.

I'll let you know when that is — or if I end up falling by the wayside and starting again, though I do hope that won't turn out to be the case! ■

John's Midnight Snack

I hate to admit it,
but sometimes Anne is right
about what not to eat!

'M in trouble again. I thought Anne had gone upstairs to bed and that I had the kitchen to myself.

I was wrong. She had forgotten her hair net and came back.

I'd cut up some cheese rind — I'll tell you about that in a minute — and I put it in a wee pan with some milk. Experimenting, I added salt and pepper and some mustard. It smelled good . . .

"You'd better add cornflour if you want that to thicken."

I jumped. I hadn't heard Anne come into the kitchen.

"Your sins will find you out!" She laughed. "You'd better put that concoction on toast. It'll never stay in a sandwich."

I really enjoyed my "concoction". But I said I would tell you about the rind of cheese . . .

When I was about ten years old, we paid a visit to Leigh in Lancashire.

On the way down, we stopped at Penrith and Ma dragged me round the shops.

We went into a high-class grocer's. You could tell it was high-class by the delicious smells.

As we stood waiting for whatever Mother wanted to buy, a gentleman ordered a thick rasher of ham.

After they had agreed on the thickness of the slice, the grocer cut it by hand. It was really thick. Price — one shilling in real money.

A shilling! To me that was a fortune. If he could afford to pay that for a slice of ham, he must be a millionaire!

A relation of Anne's died recently and she felt we should go to Kirkby Lonsdale for the funeral.

On the way back, we decided to take a break for a cup of coffee at Penrith.

Would you believe it, the high-class grocer's was still there in the square!

I dragged Anne in. She says I'll go into any shop that sells food.

The selection of cheeses was out of this world. I came away with a whole Stilton!

That night I thought Anne was already in bed, I went to the fridge for my nightly titbit. There was the Stilton with its scooped-out middle and tall, upstanding sides. What would it taste like if I sliced some into bits and boiled them in milk?

I really enjoyed my snack, despite Anne's intervention. I slept well until just after three o'clock, when something in my tummy woke me up. It couldn't be the Stilton, could it?

I heard four strike on our grandfather clock in the hall. Then five.

I got up just after six.

"Had a good night, dear?"

That was Anne, hoping the Stilton had kept me awake.

"Couldn't have slept better, dear."

Well, what would you have done?

Still, I'll be sorry when our Penrith Stilton is finished . . . ◼

119

A Cottage Industry

I have a business proposition which I bet would be a big success!

I HEREBY give notice to all those manufacturers of Scottish shortbread that they are in for some stiff competition. Anne Taylor is considering going into business — quite by accident, I may add.

Didn't a famous marmalade maker start in business in Dundee because her husband had bought too many oranges? It sold like hot cakes so she made more and more.

Anne hasn't started selling yet, but I can see it happening. The first batch, however, will be distributed among the family.

"Paul likes shortbread," Anne announced out of the blue one day. "I think I'll make some."

I read out the recipe the way she likes me to when she's baking, remembering to double everything.

Anne always doubles. She's a most economical sort and has always said that if you're going to put the oven on you may as well get your money's worth from the heat.

In any case, as she says, it's handy in case anyone drops in.

She always doubles her sponge sandwiches and as they're so light and out of this world I never complain. I'm only sorry she's given up sprinkling thin sugar on the top.

"It gets into the carpet," she always tells me, "and besides, you could do with cutting down."

Well, it never seems to get near the carpet in my case. It's usually down my front!

But getting back to Anne's shortbread.

"Seems rather a lot of flour, dear," I observed at one point — rather tentatively, as I could see Anne was frowning.

Anne had to get three big bowls — two to put flour in and one to sift into.

We were halfway through the operation — too late to draw back and reduce the ingredients — and we were beginning to flag a bit.

"John, I don't think I should have doubled it," Anne admitted. I agreed but didn't dare say so.

"It'll be handy over Christmas," I said cheerfully. "Does it keep?"

"It does if you leave it alone." Anne laughed. She's very quick at times.

Well, we got out six sandwich tins, two long flat tins and a large oval tin.

Anne rolled out the shortbread, placed it in the tins, neatly pinched it round the edges and pricked it with a fork.

It was really beautiful and just melted in the mouth — not that she let much melt in mine.

Actually, I don't think we'll bother going into business. Even making a simple thing like shortbread results in a lot of mess, and as I'm chief washer-upper, I don't think it's such a good idea! ■

John Gets A Grilling!

There's no doubt about it —
I've really done it this time!

ANNE says I'm impatient. Perhaps she's right. When I set out to do things, I like to get on with them and get them done. She says we've hardly finished a meal before I'm clearing the table.

More than once, she says, I've started a sinkful of dishes before she's even finished her last course!

Anne maintains we should sit and let our food digest. Me? I can't sit and relax until I've done the washing up.

One of Anne's friends from St Andrews never does any washing up until she's used every dish and pan in the kitchen. I once saw her sink and fled.

Anne was cross with me on the way home.

"John, you should have offered to wash up for the poor soul," she said.

Poor soul? If she had washed up after every meal she wouldn't have got into that mess!

We had come back from church and changed out of our Sunday clothes — Anne because she was going to fry haddock and me simply because I feel better in my old togs.

"Like chips, dear?"

"Yes, please!"

I like my chips. I always have done. But what a price they are these days!

Anne and I were in Cupar one night and passed the fish and chip shop. A delicious aroma filled the air.

"Oh, John, go and get a poke of chips!"

I went and joined the queue and eventually it was my turn.

"Salt and vinegar?"

"Yes, please."

The lassie put the chips into a blue box-like thing.

"Could you put them in two boxes? I'll pay for the second one."

The lassie gave me such a look . . . poor soul, can't afford two lots of chips, let alone a fish supper.

But she divided the chips and Anne and I sat in the car and ate them. They were very good — but not as good as they would have been out of a newspaper!

Anyway, back to that Sunday. I got the chips out of the deep freeze, spread them on a baking tray and put them under the grill.

Anne started to fry the Pittenweem haddock but, for some reason, the chips wouldn't cook. I put the tray one step up on the grill.

In less than a minute there was smoke and flames billowing out into the kitchen.

When an emergency arises, you tend to pick up the nearest object to hand, don't you?

Unfortunately, it was one of Anne's newest "People's Friend" tea towels. I made a grab for the chip tray and the towel went into the flames.

Anne's best towel! Why hadn't I grabbed the oven cloth?

I suppose I could have taken my time, picked up the oven cloth and pulled out the chips. By then someone would have sent for the fire brigade!

Anne, of course, had plenty to say about it — but at least I can order another tea towel for her! ▪

Compliments To The Chef!

I reckon Anne missed her calling as she gives a dinner party.

"A PENNY for them?" I asked Anne.

She looked across and smiled.

"I don't think they're worth a penny. I was thinking it's time we had someone in for a meal."

I remembered one party she gave. There must have been about sixteen couples there, but only two asked us back!

So much for the theory that you must give to receive.

So now I suggested to Anne that we ask a couple round for dinner. But I was duly quashed. Anne didn't want to invite just one couple.

The last time we'd done that, the husband and I had talked farming all night, and then we'd gone down to the byre to take a look at the cows.

Not the evening Anne had had in mind.

So we decided to invite two couples, and once we'd finished arguing about who they should be, the next problem was the menu.

Give Anne her due, she's a great cook and, when entertaining, she likes to be original.

I suggested soup, prawn cocktail, egg

mayonnaise or potted shrimps for starters. They all got the thumbs down. You'd think we had them every day.

"John, I'm going to give them baked haddock with sauce Antonia," she said at last.

You can always rely on Anne to come up with something different.

We had haddock in the deep freeze so I didn't have to rush to Pittenweem. A pity, really, as I enjoy the harbour, the boats and the fish market.

Well, Anne got the haddock out and left it on a plate to defrost overnight.

I pointed out that they were very small haddock. Anne showed me how she'd divide them among six of us.

"Darling, you can't give them that wee bit," I cried.

"You only get a mouthful at a hotel," Anne pointed out.

Well, those six wee pieces of haddock were cooked with great care. I bet if she'd overdone them, they'd have shrunk.

Anne buttered a piece of silver foil, dotted each piece of haddock with butter, and folded the foil over them.

She said there was nothing unusual about her Antonia sauce, but I noticed she made it with great care and followed the recipe.

It not only looked good, but it tasted out of this world. There are times when I just have to hand it to my Anne, and this was one of them.

Those six wee bits of haddock, spead out on a hot serving plate, all covered in the pink sauce plus wedges of lemon and fresh parsley, looked as though they'd been made by the top chef at Gleneagles.

Well, they'd been made by the top chef at the Riggin. The guests were very impressed and like me, I bet, could have eaten three times the amount.

Do you find it's those little details that you remember best? ∎

Sweet
And Sour

**My bargains from the
supermarket met with a
sour look from Anne!**

'M slimming. Anne would say who's kidding who, but I've gone in for buying lots of fruit when I'm in Cupar on my own. I'm told it's good for the figure, and mine needs it.

I really called in for some onions — good for soup and tripe — and carrots, but I got carried away with the bargains.

I bought ten grapefruit plus oranges, apples and a goodly bunch of black grapes for Anne.

Oh, and I added three bananas to my basket. There's no such thing as a penny banana these days, is there?

Anne says that when she was young she once called in at the village shop and bought a penny banana. Yes, just one banana.

When she handed over to her mother the money from the sale of the eggs and butter, less what she had bought, her mum said she was a penny short.

Anne admitted she had bought a banana. She got one of those tellings-off she would never forget.

It wasn't the fact that Anne had spent the penny that worried her mum, but that she had left her to find out for herself that the money was short.

Anyway, coming back to my slimming . . .

When I got home and opened my bag of fruit, was I thanked?

Not a bit of it. In a voice that would have turned the cream sour, Anne said, "John, you love to cover my worktop with fruit."

I said nothing, but she was right — I do!

Well, I put out my ten grapefruit. Like Queen Victoria, Anne was not amused. I get into trouble for trying to do things which Anne sees as her job.

"You look after the farm and I'll look after the house, John!" she always tells me. "Leave the groceries to me!"

But I enjoy eating, and I can't resist a bargain in the food line.

Sometimes, though, she has been known to cut a grapefruit in half, sprinkle it with brown sugar and put it under the grill. They are very good.

Anne says it's all right in summer, but in winter we have porridge.

What went through my mind when I saw my bargain grapefruit was whether they could be eaten in segments, like oranges.

Well, tonight I peeled one. It was out of this world — sour, but it gave you the feeling of having tasted something nature meant you to eat and enjoy.

Will it help me weigh less? I don't know, but I'm going back for more!

I'm eating more fruit these days, and Anne approves because she thinks I'm doing it to bring my weight down.

But the truth is, I eat it because I enjoy it — but don't tell Anne, will you? ◼

John takes time to appreciate nature's beauty.

The Old Ways

To The Manner Born!

I know the difference between right and wrong – my granny taught me!

J OHN TAYLOR, didn't your mother teach you any manners?"
This outburst took place in the passage leading to the back door.
Anne had slammed the door shut and I knew by this that there was trouble in store. I didn't think that I'd put a foot wrong all evening, but it seemed I had.

Anne had asked two couples in for a Saturday night dinner and a blether.

I hadn't talked farming and I hadn't taken the men to see the young bull I'd just bought. For the life of me I couldn't think what I'd done wrong.

I put my lack of airs and graces down to the fact that I was an only child. In other words, I hadn't a sister who could have told me how to behave when it came to the female sex.

I remember being filled with trepidation at being kissed by a young lassie with bows in her hair at a birthday party!

In fact, I continued to be frightened of girls until I met Anne.

But to get back to my story.

When the first couple came through the back door, Joan handed Anne a parcel and Ian gave Anne a big kiss. I took Joan's coat. I knew that much, at least!

Mary and Gavin were next. Gavin put his arms around my Anne and he, too, gave her a kiss. I can't remember if I took Mary's coat but I'm quite sure I didn't kiss her.

When they left, both men kissed Anne in a very friendly fashion, to my way of thinking.

Now I learned that Anne was annoyed because she thought I should have done as they'd done and kissed the women as they entered and left.

I'll be honest, I'm no good at this silly kissing of other men's wives. Perhaps there's something wrong with me, but I never remember visitors kissing Mother on our farm. I think Dad would have got out of his chair and walloped them one!

It just wasn't done to go around kissing other men's wives, not least in front of them!

As I was up the top fields the next day I took a moment to lean on the dyke and think about manners.

Granny, bless her, taught me everything I know. We always said grace before a meal and couldn't leave the table without saying "Thank you" or "May I".

Sunday dinner at Granny's, after attending the Methodist chapel, was a wonderful affair, and the table was always set with a starched, white linen cloth and white serviettes folded in the form of a waterlily.

Since those days, I've never seen anything starched the way Granny did it – ironed with an iron into which she slipped a hot clog.

Granny taught me to pray and read the Bible, but, thank goodness, she didn't teach me to kiss men's wives at the drop of a hat – and I've no intention of starting now, even for Anne! ◼

Rag Rugs And Brown Paper

Sometimes the old ways are the best – don't you agree?

"YOU shouldn't laugh at your betters!"

Believe it or not, that wasn't Anne talking to me — it was me talking to Anne!

"Are you implying you're my better?" she asked disdainfully.

Well, of course, I wasn't brave enough to go any further down that road. I just glowered at her instead.

"You could try helping instead of laughing," I said.

"Admit it — you've lost your touch, John," Anne told me.

She was right, of course, but I was doing my best to make a neat job of it.

I was trying, very awkwardly, to cover a book with brown paper. Both Anne and I used to cover everything when we were at school. Somehow we had more respect for things in those days, even a twopenny exercise book.

Talking of things past, I expect many readers will remember having a duster bag which accepted all the old vests which had been darned till they couldn't be darned any more.

We also had a rug bag. Into it went old jackets, trousers, anything that could later be washed, cut up and made into a pegged rug.

"Anne, what happened to our pegged rug?" I asked.

"It got old, like you, and fell to bits."

Charming!

It was the custom in our day that when a

134

young couple fixed their wedding day, the girl's family would set to and peg a rug. The rug bag was tipped out and one or two of the girls cut the pieces to the right length.

If four people got round a table with a log fire burning and an oil lamp shining from the beam above, it was surprising how quickly they could finish one.

I wonder if anyone still pegs rugs nowadays. It would be a shame to lose such a craft.

To come back to my problem of covering a book.

It was a book I'd been dying to read, but I wanted to keep it and its jacket like new before giving it as a present to our son, Paul. It would make an ideal gift for his birthday, which was coming up soon.

It's now covered, after a fashion. I may be losing my touch, but that's hardly surprising. After all, I'm not sixteen any more! ■

Penny For Your Thoughts

When my Anne starts reminiscing, her memories are worth much more than that . . .

PENNY for them," I said.

Anne was sitting in her Orkney chair, staring into space. She smiled and came back down to earth.

"I was back at home in our kitchen when I was a lass."

I could remember that well, too. I always used to go to Anne's on a Sunday night, but once I popped in on a Friday.

It was baking night, and the aroma of fresh bread and cakes was out of this world.

Anne handed me a hot, buttered scone. I can still remember the taste, all these years later.

Looking back, Anne remembers them baking twelve or fourteen loaves for the week. They also made gingerbreads in large loaf tins, and big plate pies filled with apples, plums or whatever was in season.

How they managed such a baking I do not know. They only had a small oven with two shelves by the side of the open fire, which was wood-burning.

Anne and I really enjoyed looking back that evening. She reminded me of how her family had bought flour in half-hundredweight bags. The bags were washed and used afterwards as pillow-slips.

Anne, like her mum before her, is a real expert at Yorkshire pudding.

I have always understood — but I'm sure some farmer's wife from Yorkshire will correct me if I'm wrong — that the mistress of the farm made a great big Yorkshire pudding in a flat tin and served it as the first course. This would fill them up so they didn't need so much meat.

Anne does the same when "the boys" are coming. But they seem to eat just as much anyway!

It was just as we were getting ready for bed that she reminded me.

"John, I must make a Dundee cake."

"Yes, dear, you said that at breakfast."

She'd just found her cake tins empty. And that would never do. I know my Anne so well.

She would have felt she had let her mother down if someone had called and she couldn't offer them something home-made – only a biscuit out of a packet.

And when Anne says she must make a Dundee cake, she doesn't mean only one cake.

She never does things by half. Oh, yes, a Dundee cake would be made, but there would be two plate pies, two sponges and, I hope, to use up the heat, she would put in an egg custard.

I love Anne's egg custards with a grating of nutmeg on top. Not good for the figure, but why worry? I enjoy eating.

"It shows," Anne says often. ■

Those Were The Days!

What did we do before microwaves and other mod cons?

LAST week I bought Anne a surprise present for the house. Well, she maintains it wasn't a present for her at all, that I bought it for myself. She has a point. Let's say it was for both of us.

Anne says it's my new toy, but I've noticed she has taken a great interest in it. Let me tell you how I came to buy it before I tell you what it is!

Alice, a neighbouring farmer's wife, had bumped into Anne in Anstruther and asked us up for something to eat and a blether on the Friday night.

We went, and supper consisted of home-cooked ham and jacket potatoes.

"And they took just six minutes to cook," Alice commented.

Anne gave her one of those looks which said, "Try pulling the other leg!"

What we didn't know then was that Alice had recently invested in a microwave oven. And she praised it so highly that I reckoned there must be something in it — Alice isn't really one for keeping up with the Joneses.

After supper, she offered to give us a practical demonstration and we were suitably impressed — there were no pans to wash up, either.

The following Tuesday I called in at the electricity showroom in St Andrews and bought one.

Anne took one look at the display panel and said, "I'll never master this, John."

I must admit that, at first glance, you take fright at all the buttons, and wonder if it'll blow up if you press the wrong one!

But when I came in for tea, Anne was absorbed in the manual.

"How can it scramble eggs for two in eighty seconds?" she demanded.

Well, how was I supposed to know?

But Anne tried the new microwave out making our tea, and it was a great success. Anne was delighted. She told me it took longer to toast the two slices of bread than it did to scramble the eggs!

Anne has taken to it like a duck to water. But as she said to me later, "Young folk don't know they're born, John."

It was in the Thirties when I called at Anne's farmhouse unexpectedly one Friday just after lunch.

You should have seen the spread on their kitchen table.

There were seven of them on that farm and Anne and her mother had one baking day a week. There were loaves, savoury pies and large, flat, fruit pies cut up into squares, two large gingerbreads and some cakes.

They didn't even have an electric cooker in those days. It was all made in the oven at the side of the open fire. On one side was the oven, on the other, the hot water boiler.

The kettle and a large broth pan swung on a handle over the fire. Everything had to be heated from that open fire, kept going mainly with wood.

Anne was always the earliest riser in the household and the first thing she did was clean out the fire, light it and boil the kettle to take her mum and dad a cup of tea in bed. No flick of an electric switch then.

We've come a long way from those days. But are folk today as happy as we were way back then? ■

John and Jip keep an eye on the flock.

Published in Great Britain by D.C. Thomson & Co., Ltd., 185 Fleet Street, London EC4A 2HS
© D.C. Thomson & Co. Ltd. 2016
Tel. 01382 223 131
www.dcthomson.co.uk